General Editor: M. Rolf Olsen

TAVISTOCK LIBRARY OF SOCIAL WORK PRACTICE

Child Psychiatry
and
Social Work

Child Psychiatry and Social Work

JUDITH LASK
& BRYAN LASK

TAVISTOCK PUBLICATIONS
London and New York

First published in 1981 by
Tavistock Publications Ltd
11 New Fetter Lane, London EC4P 4EE
Published in the USA by
Tavistock Publications
in association with Methuen, Inc.
733 Third Avenue, New York, NY 10017

© 1981 Judith Lask and Bryan Lask
General editor's foreword © 1981 M. Rolf Olsen

Photoset by
Nene Phototypesetters Ltd, Northampton
and printed in Great Britain by
Richard Clay (The Chaucer Press) Ltd
Bungay, Suffolk

British Library Cataloguing in Publication Data

Lask, Judith
Child psychiatry and social work. – (Tavistock
library of social work practice; SSP 219)
1. Child psychiatry
I. Title   II. Lask, Bryan   III. Series
618.92′89′024362   RJ499

ISBN 0–422–77080–9
ISBN 0–422–77090–6 Pbk

Contents

General editor's foreword *vii*
Acknowledgements *xi*
Preface *xiii*

1 Background *1*
2 Causation *11*
3 Assessment *27*
4 Common presenting problems *54*
5 Family and marital therapy *94*
6 Individual casework, counselling, and
    individual psychotherapy *117*
7 Groupwork and group therapy *131*
8 Behaviour modification *138*
9 Consultation and liaison *154*
10 Environmental change and alternative
    forms of care *162*
11 Medication *172*
    Case illustration *176*

References *181*
Name index *200*
Subject index *204*

General editor's foreword

Tavistock Library of Social Work Practice is a new series of books primarily written for practitioners and students of social work and the personal social services, but also for those who work in the allied fields of health, education, and other public services. The series represents the collaborative effort of social work academics, practitioners, and managers. In addition to considering the theoretical and philosophical debate surrounding the topics under consideration, the texts are firmly rooted in practice issues and the problems associated with the organization of the services. Therefore the series will be of particular value to undergraduate and post-graduate students of social work and social administration.

The series was prompted by the growth and increasing importance of the social services in our society. Until recently there has been a general approbation of social work, reflected in a benedictory increase in manpower and resources, which has led to an unprecedented expansion of the personal social services, a proliferation of the statutory duties placed upon them, and major reorganization. The result has been the emergence of a profession faced with the immense responsibilities of promoting individual and social betterment, and bearing a primary responsibility to advocate on behalf of individuals and groups who do not always fulfil or respect normal social expectations of behaviour. In spite of the growth in services these tasks are often carried out with inadequate resources, an uncertain knowledge base, and as yet unresolved difficulties associated with the reorganization of the personal social services in 1970. In recent years these difficulties have been compounded by a level of criticism unprecedented since the Poor Law. The anti-social work critique has fostered some improbable alliances between groups of social administrators, sociologists, doctors, and the media, united in their belief that social work has failed in its general obligation to 'provide services to the people', and in its particular duty to socialize the delinquent, restrain parents who abuse their children, prevent old people from dying alone, and provide a satisfactory level of community care for the sick, the chronically handicapped, and the mentally disabled.

These developments highlight three major issues that deserve particular attention. First, is the need to construct a methodology for analysing social and personal situations and prescribing action; second, is the necessity to apply techniques that measure the performance of the individual worker and the profession as a whole in meeting stated objectives; third, and outstanding, is the requirement to develop a knowledge base against which the needs of clients are understood and decisions about their care are taken. Overall, the volumes in this series make explicit and clarify these issues; contribute to the search for the distinctive knowledge base of social work; increase our understanding of the aetiology and care of personal, familial, and social problems; describe and explore new techniques and practice skills; aim to raise our commitment towards low status groups which suffer public, political, and professional neglect; and to promote the enactment of comprehensive and socially just policies. Above all, these volumes aim to promote an understanding which interprets the needs of individuals, groups, and communities in terms of the synthesis between inner needs and the social realities that impinge upon them, and which aspire to develop informed and skilled practice.

M. ROLF OLSEN
Birmingham University
1981

To Gideon and Adam
who are so pleased that we
have completed this book.

Acknowledgements

We wish to convey our most sincere gratitude to:

Our many friends and colleagues at Great Ormond Street and the Maudsley who have nurtured, influenced, taught, and tolerated us, and especially Lionel Hersov and Judy Treseder who introduced us!

Rolf Olsen who provided invaluable advice during the preparation of this book.

Rita Nani who not only laboured over the manuscript but patiently coped with all our panics.

Preface

This book is intended as a broad introduction to the assessment and management of child-focused problems. Although it is written as part of a social work series, we anticipate it will be of value to all students and professionals involved in the well-being of children. Child psychiatry is concerned with the child who is suffering emotionally, whose development is delayed, or whose behaviour causes concern to others. It has therefore much in common with aspects of social work practice. Although the two professions have worked closely together there have often been considerable theoretical differences reflected in their modes of practice. We are convinced that there should be a common approach which embraces the special contributions of each. Any professional who encounters child-focused problems should bring with him a detailed understanding of causation (at an individual, family, and societal level), an ability to make a comprehensive assessment, a knowledge of a wide variety of intervention techniques, and the skill to undertake at least some of them.

In this book we provide a basic knowledge of the common child-focused problems, offer a framework for understanding the causes, and discuss methods of assessment and intervention. Our orientation is firmly based on the family approach, in which due consideration is given not only to the family relationships but also to the complex interaction between the child, his family, and the environment. Special emphasis is placed on intervention and management because in our opinion most books dealing with child-focused problems give far too little attention to this important area. Theoretical understanding is of little use, if, at the point of contact, the professional flounders. We outline and discuss the main skills and techniques commonly used in such problems and refer to any useful evaluative work. We describe child-focused problems only up to adolescence, deliberately excluding problems specific to older adolescents, and also to children with physical or mental handicap. These groups present particular problems and demand special resources, although the principles involved in assessment and management are much the same as for the other groups.

A number of case examples are used to illustrate various points but the names have been changed and the circumstances disguised. For the sake of convenience the term 'she' is used when we refer to the social worker, and 'he' when we refer either to any other professional, or to the child, unless the circumstances demand otherwise. Numerous references are made throughout the text and we have attempted to include a comprehensive cross-reference system.

We hope this book will inspire its readers to try new ways of working, to evaluate what they do, and to share bravely their successes and failures with others, so that we may all continue to learn, develop our skills, and make a positive contribution to the healthy development of this and future generations.

1
Background

Introduction

Our main aim in writing this book is to afford assistance to both students and professionals who find themselves faced with child-focused problems. The fields of psychiatry, psychology, and social work, as they relate·to childhood problems, are complex. Amongst the many and diverse theories of child development are those derived from the psychoanalytic, learning, and Piagetian schools. Techniques of intervention reflect this diversity, and include behaviour modification, different forms of psychotherapy, environmental changes, and the prescribing of medicines. The main focus of attention may be the child, parents, whole family, school, community, or, more likely, a combination of a number of these. The professionals involved may include social workers, psychologists, psycho-therapists, psychiatrists, teachers, educational welfare officers, school counsellors, health visitors, nurses, doctors, and others.

We are writing for a wide range of people who vary considerably in their training, knowledge, skills, experience, philosophy, values, and agency setting. Instead of dealing specifically with the opportunities and limitations afforded by different agency settings, we have chosen to outline what we consider to be the more useful, appropriate, and effective ways of working with this group of clients. There is no reason why ideally these cannot be used in most settings. We have emphasized techniques such as family therapy and behaviour modification which we know are difficult to implement in some agencies for various reasons. We do this because we consider such methods to be effective, and efforts should therefore be made to make them available. We discuss other techniques such as individual psychotherapy and casework because, although they are of uncertain value, they are in common use.

Flexibility is essential for any worker in this field. When assessing a problem, he must consider all aspects of a child's life and environment. Further, he should be familiar with the possibilities of a whole range of intervention techniques. He is unlikely to possess the knowledge and skills to practise them all, but he should understand them and be able to enlist the help of others when necessary.

Certain fundamental issues influence the quality and effectiveness of the help provided for child-centred problems. In the remainder of this chapter we give some consideration to a number of important points as a background to the rest of the book.

Provisions for the disturbed child and his family

Provisions for the disturbed child and his family arise from a variety of sources and are under the control of many different organizations, often with variation between areas. The local authority provides direct social work to families, community work, and alternative forms of care as well as intermediate treatment, parent and young people's groups, and other schemes which particular departments may provide. Education authorities usually provide most of the child guidance clinics, nursery schools, the school psychological service, school counsellors, educational welfare officers, teachers with pastoral care functions, special schools, and various schemes for dealing with truancy and other school problems. Area health authorities normally provide the child psychiatric service, school medical officers, paediatricians, general practitioners, and health visitors. In addition to these, there are numerous voluntary organizations and self-help groups. Further help (as well as the opposite) can come from any of a family's many resource systems such as friends, neighbourhood, clubs, place of employment, police, or school. Certainly there is strength in having this variety of different approaches and it is vital that there is a universal understanding of the difficulties and problems that children and families can have.

Unfortunately, this shared responsibility often leads to a patchy and unco-ordinated service.

THE CHILD GUIDANCE CLINIC AND CHILD PSYCHIATRIC DEPARTMENT

In this country, the first child guidance clinics were set up in the 1920s following the establishment of similar clinics in the United States of America. The clinics aimed to serve community needs (Kanner 1959) and the basic team of psychiatrist, psychologist, and social worker was constituted in response to the need for an inter-disciplinary approach. A few hospital-based clinics existed before 1948, but the majority were developed after the setting up of the National Health Service. The Education Act 1944 requires local education authorities to provide a medical service which covers both the physical and psychological needs of children. The present child guidance clinics are usually the joint responsibility of the local education authorities (who employ the psychologists, teachers, and sometimes the social workers) and the area health authorities (who employ the psychiatrists). The clinic is usually directed by a psychiatrist or psychologist. The structure of hospital departments is very similar, although always with a doctor in charge. Such departments often have access to in-patient beds and work closely with paediatricians.

One of the most frequent criticisms of the child guidance service is that clinics remain isolated from the community. This arises partly from the inaccessibility of many clinics (both to clients and pro-fessionals) except through a lengthy referral system. The frequently long waiting lists mean that help is often unavailable at the point of crisis, and the limited availability of appointment times can also create difficulties for clients. Further, clinics do not always take full account of the role of social and environmental factors, either in relation to causation or to intervention, despite the fact that social workers have always been an integral part of the clinic team. This may be because clinic social workers have tended to differ from other social workers in their greater emphasis on the psychoanalytic approach (Sussenwein 1976), their generally higher training, and their adherence to casework as the main form of intervention.

4   Child Psychiatry and Social Work

As mentioned earlier, local authorities provide many services either directly or indirectly for the troubled child and his family. One study of two long-term social service teams (Goldberg *et al* 1978) showed that 'problems of child behaviour and social relationships' constituted 35 per cent of all individual caseloads and demanded a high level of contact. These clients were usually involved with other agencies and the outcome of these cases was rarely positive. This illustrates the fact that this group of clients presents a real challenge to social workers who are struggling with huge caseloads, lack of resources, uncertain knowledge, and overwhelming social and economic pressures on clients.

Local authority social service departments come in for criticism from almost everyone, including child psychiatrists, psychologists, and clinic and hospital social workers. One of the main criticisms is the lack of clear thinking in the assessment of problems, and another, the frequent inappropriate referral for specialist help, often emphasizing the labelling of a particular child as 'mad' or 'bad' to facilitate a referral. Local authority social workers often take a limited view of interventions, and little groupwork, family therapy, or behaviour modification, is carried out.

TOWARDS A BETTER SERVICE

Child guidance clinics are making many changes, although some still remain very traditional in their approach. Many are offering a more immediate service, accepting 'self referrals' and even operating 'walk-in clinics'. Some are developing their consultancy functions (Mills 1979) and working closely with other professionals, often outside the confines of the clinic. Now that social workers are generically trained and those in hospitals and some clinics are employed by the local authority, there is more appreciation of social and environmental influences on clients. This greater communication is also helping each to understand the other's work and to decrease unrealistic expectations.

Methods of work are beginning to change in all agencies, with a welcome move towards more planned, focused, and short-term work. One offshoot of the growth of family therapy as a technique has been the sharing of its development between different professions and the growth of a common language. We would like to see a continuation of all these trends, coupled with more evaluation of interventions and joint participation in the planning of resources and training programmes. In many settings training is all too often undervalued, and yet, however good the facilities, a lack of skills and knowledge is bound to affect adversely the quality of the service provided.

We consider that much work at present done in specialist clinics could be carried out in the community, but this would mean adjustments being made in training and the allocation of resources. Certainly, local authorities have a strong role to play in the provision of facilities such as day-nurseries and day-centres for mothers and children, community work, and the development of their advocacy functions to help remove some of the burdensome pressures that many families have to bear. Certainly, all workers, in the clinic or in the community, must continue to broaden the base of their assessment and interventions.

The family approach

Amongst those working with disturbed children are adherents to a variety of theoretical models. Some faithfully pursue one particular approach (for example, psychoanalytic or behavioural), while others are more eclectic. Human behaviour is so complex that no theory or intervention has yet encompassed all its dimensions, and therefore we advocate a broad-based and eclectic approach, which gives due consideration to all relevant factors. Few would dispute the central role of the family (natural or substitute) in the life of the child, and this leads us to look at the family as a first step in understanding a child's difficulties. Essentially, we view the family as an interacting system, and just as a child is largely what he is because he is part of that particular system, so the family is part of a larger interacting societal system. Pincus and Minahan (1973) advocate the consideration of all systems infringing upon a client, and view them all as possible targets for intervention. Basically, we agree with their view, although maintaining that they place too little emphasis on the potency of the highly charged family system.

The implication of this approach for intervention is that whenever possible the family, rather than the child, is taken on as client. This does not mean that family therapy is always the most appropriate intervention technique (although frequently it is, either on its own or coupled with other interventions). Often changes need to be made in the home, school, or social environment. Other techniques, such as group therapy or behaviour modification may also be indicated. However, research findings steadily underline the place of family therapy as one of the few techniques which are seen to be effective, and we agree with Walrond-Skinner (1976) that it would be unfortunate if family therapy was rejected by social workers as 'precious' or irrelevant, before its potential has been sufficiently examined. Often families, freed from the paralysis and pain within the family, can themselves find solutions to outside problems.

The social work contribution

Social work practice has changed a good deal over recent years. From a reliance on psychoanalytic theory and casework methods, social work has encompassed other theories and a variety of interventions. Its targets of intervention have widened from the individual and the family to include schools, community, and, latterly, all of a client's resource systems. This is, however, a general trend, and the profession encompasses people working in many different ways. In the child guidance clinic the role of the social worker has also changed. Her traditional role of working only with parents is gradually expanding, so that in many clinics she now works with all members of the family and uses a variety of techniques. The growth of family therapy owes a great deal to social workers, and has led to a further breakdown of the boundaries between different professions. However, social workers in child guidance settings have been less concerned with community work and welfare rights, and have often failed to contribute a knowledge of these to the clinic team.

In examining the contribution that social work can make to helping the disturbed child and his family, we consider the main strength to lie in the ability of the profession to encompass an awareness of the interaction between the child, his family, and the environment. Translated into help for clients, this implies an acceptance of all aspects of that interaction as possible targets for intervention techniques.

As in other professions, specialization inevitably occurs. One worker may be more interested in the individual or the family, another in welfare rights, and a third may specialize in one particular intervention technique. However, an awareness that a client's problems are an interaction between client, family, and environment must remain, if a social worker is to have something unique to add to the work of fellow professionals. The social work profession has a valuable contribution to make to the balanced development of services, and must make a larger contribution in the fields of research and prevention.

Research

Among the helping professions, opinions abound but hard evidence is lacking. For many years the fields of child psychiatry and social work were influenced by practitioners with a psychodynamic orientation who denied the need for convincing evidence to support their firmly-held beliefs. In child psychiatry there has developed a backlash, the result of which is that many practitioners consider that nothing can be taken for granted, and everything must be proven. Studies have become highly sophisticated and any that are not based on rigorous scientific principles are subject to considerable criticism. Gradually, a balance is being restored, and many would agree with Frude (1980) that, by placing undue emphasis on perfect methodology, useful information arising from less stringent studies is being ignored. This debate is bound to affect social work for it is unrealistic to compartmentalize the results of research into different professions. Further, those social workers with little or no training in research methodology are unlikely to initiate large-scale projects.

There has been an unfortunate polarization between researchers and those working with clients. Researchers doubt the value of intervention techniques and practitioners are frustrated by the researchers' insistence on methodological perfection. This has resulted in a large amount of research into the characteristics of normal development, the incidence of different types of emotional and behavioural problems, and the outcome in adult life of childhood disturbance. No one would dispute the relevance of such studies, but equally relevant and largely ignored is the whole area of treatment outcome.

It is important to question the value of our work with clients, and as various treatment studies have produced somewhat discouraging results (for example, Fischer 1976, Goldberg 1973) we must be wary of all but the most modest claims for our effectiveness. There is, however, a number of studies indicating the usefulness of both behaviour modification techniques and of family therapy, which we discuss in the relevant chapters. Further, Reid and Shyne (1969) have shown that casework is more effective if it is short-term, active, and focused, rather than long-term, passive, and unfocused.

The methodological problems related to outcome research are enormous. Nonetheless, it is perfectly possible, using a simple technique, to incorporate an evaluation of intervention (Baird 1978, Lask 1980). (We discuss this further in Chapter 5.) Such a technique could be extended to work with small and large groups. This critical self-appraisal is a prerequisite for good work and a starting point for more ambitious studies. Further, the collection of such basic data as type and mode of referral, method of intervention and outcome, may show patterns that have implications for further action. For example, if an excess of referrals come from one school, it may be of value to allocate a member of the agency to act as a consultant to that school; similarly, a housing estate, giving rise to many problems might benefit from the help of a community worker.

Prevention

Prevention is a generally neglected area, and yet it is clearly preferable to prevent a problem from arising, especially when evidence suggests that many interventions meet with little success. Caplan (1964) defines prevention on three levels: primary prevention which includes measures to reduce the incidence of problems in groups as yet unaffected, secondary prevention which aims at early identification of problems and rapid intervention, and tertiary prevention which includes measures taken once a problem is established to limit its duration and intensity. Obviously, social work has a role to play in all three areas.

Preventive measures can be taken in individual cases – for example, a nursery place for a child who may be at risk – or involve large-scale operations such as the up-grading of a housing estate. Large-scale measures must be assessed for cost-effectiveness and based on firm evidence. All such projects should involve measures for their own evaluation. A great deal more has to be known about the reasons for childhood problems and why some children do manage to survive the most disadvantageous environment, while others do not, and suffer.

However, even in the present state of knowledge, there are many areas where preventive measures could be employed. It is probable that a disruption in the early mother-baby relationship interferes with the 'bonding' process, and this might well be a factor contributing to later anti-social behaviour (Rutter 1972). The implication of this is that mothers should not be separated from their babies unless absolutely necessary and that special help should be given if separation is unavoidable. Better ante-natal and maternity care would also help by cutting down the risk of brain damage. Children who are chronically ill or have handicaps are more likely to develop emotional difficulties. Measures could be taken to reduce the risk of illness and accidents as well as to provide help, support, and good hospital facilities for this group. Liaison schemes with paediatricians could be very helpful. Characteristics of the community such as bad housing and poor schools are associated with a high level of problems. Improvements in these areas could have very beneficial effects. Children who have been in care also represent a vulnerable group and this vulnerability seems to be associated with the quality of care (Barker 1979). Clearly, the provision of excellent alternative care would be of great value. The quality of parental care appears to be of crucial significance and a great deal more needs to be done in terms of general education for parenthood, and better support systems for parents with young children.

These are just a few of the areas where preventive projects would be useful. The scope of this field is enormous and a more active role should be taken not only by local and central government but also by individual agencies and workers who can feed-back information and press for necessary action, as well as plan small, evaluated projects themselves.

Conclusions

When considering child-focused problems, issues of major importance include the quality of the available service, the need for a comprehensive approach with particular emphasis on the family, the special contribution of the social worker, the necessity for additional training and good supervision, the need for further research in various areas but particularly in relation to evaluation of interventions, and the possibilities for prevention. Each of these themes is discussed in this chapter and should be considered in relation to succeeding chapters.

2
Causation

Introduction

When considering the origins of childhood disturbance there are no simple cause-and-effect relationships. Indeed, there are many different ways of conceptualizing the complex processes of normal and abnormal child development. Amongst the most influential theories have been maturational (e.g. Gesell 1954), Piagetian (e.g. Furth 1969), psychoanalytic (e.g. Smirnoff 1971), ethological (e.g. Bowlby 1975) and learning (see Chapter 8). This myriad of differing conceptualizations makes the task of considering the causes of emotional, behavioural, and developmental problems particularly complex. In addition, there are profound methodological difficulties in determining the significance of any potential causative factors (Liederman, Tulkin, and Rosenfeld 1977).

In this chapter we consider some of the factors thought adversely to influence the psycho-social development of children. It is worth noting that some factors are equally important in all cultures, whilst others may be culture-specific. Further, factors which *cause* a psychological disorder may differ from those factors which *perpetuate* it. For example, a child may develop severe behavioural difficulties as a result of earlier experience of deprivation, but the problem may be perpetuated by family handling. There is now general agreement that child development (normal and abnormal) is determined by a complex interaction between biological and environmental factors (Minde and Cohen 1979: 309) but there is wide disagreement about their relative importance.

For all these reasons we consider causation from a multi-factorial perspective, and emphasize the importance of understanding the significance of the *interaction* between factors. Therapeutic interventions discussed later in the book are based on the same model.

Environmental factors

These are best sub-divided into intrafamilial and socio-cultural, although there is considerable overlap between them.

The family

In our society the burden carried by the family is large, and many writers have tried to conceptualize its functions. Lidz (1968) describes the main tasks of the family as the provision of emotional bonds and relationships, a secure base, models of behaviour and attitudes, life experiences, the shaping of behaviour, and a communication network. Satir (1978) echoes this by saying the family is the main learning context for individual behaviour, thoughts, and feelings. Minuchin (1974) states that the family provides nurturance, guidance, and control. The family, in whatever form it takes, is as fundamental to the child as is food to life. It is hardly surprising then that much can go wrong.

(i)   EMOTIONAL BONDS AND RELATIONSHIPS

Generally, in our culture, children develop specific bonds to significant people (usually biological, adoptive, or foster-parents) as well as other relatives such as grandparents and siblings. The biological link is not essential. Although it has been suggested that very early contact (in the first few hours of life) enhances bonding, nonetheless children adopted in the first few weeks of life can develop very satisfactory bonds. The most important factors are the centrality and stability of the adult figures (Rutter 1972).

Bonds provide a pattern for future relationships. Unsatisfactory bonding may result from prolonged separation in the neonatal period due to illness in either the baby or mother, and from adverse personality or temperamental characteristics in the baby, or the biological or surrogate parents. Interruptions, due to separations as the child gets older, may also have an adverse effect. Frequent hospitalization in children under five seems to increase the chances of children later developing anti-social behaviour problems (Douglas 1975). Such children are more likely to come from socially disadvantaged families, so that possibly there is an interaction between the effects of separation and social disadvantage.

Whether such separations do adversely affect bonding is dependent upon such factors as the quality of the substitute care, the age of the child, his temperament, and how well-prepared he is for the separation. When bonding is adversely affected, both the child's ability to make satisfactory personal relationships in later life and his subsequent personality development may be impaired.

'Maternal deprivation'

The concept of maternal deprivation was brought to public attention by Bowlby (1951) when he wrote that early life experiences may have serious and lasting effects on development. Bowlby, whose conclusions were based on studies of institutionalized children, stated that maternal deprivation might have grave and far-reaching effects on a child's personality and intellect. He included a wide range of reactions to separation and loss under the term 'maternal deprivation'; acute distress, failure-to-thrive, developmental delay, intellectual impairment, enuresis, delinquency, and the inability to form emotional relationships. One major consequence of this controversial statement was the great improvement in institutional care of children. Many researchers have since questioned Bowlby's concept of maternal deprivation. One of the world's leading authorities on separation and loss in children has reviewed all the evidence for and against such a syndrome and has challenged some of Bowlby's conclusions (Rutter 1972). Rutter evokes other authorities in his own criticism of the methodology of the studies that Bowlby used, and points out that

> 'some of the supposed sequelae of deprivation might be artefacts due to the biases existing in how children are chosen to be admitted to institutions, or might be due to hereditary conditions, or might represent the consequences of biological damage.'
>
> (p. 120)

Rutter suggests that the acute distress is probably due to disruption of the bonding process (not necessarily with the mother), the failure-to-thrive is a result of poor nutrition, the developmental delay and intellectual impairment are a consequence of a lack of perceptual and linguistic stimulation, the enuresis is a reaction to early stresses, the delinquency follows family discord, and the psychopathic behaviour in adult life is the end-product of a failure to develop bonds or attachments in the first three years of life.

Rutter is also critical of the actual words used, 'maternal' and 'deprivation'. He considers that the bond between mother and infant is not qualitatively or innately different from bonds between infant and other significant adult figures. It is the culturally determined centrality of the mother that has given the false impression that the mother-infant bond is unique: 'The chief bond need not be with a biological parent, it need not be with the chief caretaker, and it need not be with a female' (Rutter 1972: 125).

Rutter also says that the term 'deprivation', which means dis-possession or loss, is misleading in that in most cases the deleterious influences are not due to deprivation. He considers that the damage comes from a *lack* or *distortion* of care rather than a loss. The term 'privation' is more accurate.

Rutter concludes that the term 'maternal deprivation' has served its purpose and should now be abandoned:

> 'bad care of children in early life can have bad effects, both short-term and long-term . . . what is now needed is a more precise delineation of the different aspects of "badness", together with an analysis of their separate effects and of the reasons why children differ in their responses.'   (p. 128)

(ii)   A SECURE BASE

Children require the security of a stable home and a stable family life. Studies have shown that there is a strong link between discordant family relationships and the development of behaviour problems in pre-school children (Richman 1977). It is probable that such children are disturbed by a combination of factors including the degree of family tension, their own involvement in the marital disharmony, the frustration of their emotional needs, and the models of aggressive, inconsistent, or depressed behaviour provided by their parents.

The death of one parent, although obviously traumatic, has less adverse effect on the child's personality development than the loss of a parent through separation. This latter is usually preceded by a long period of emotional tension and turmoil, which does not necessarily cease at the point of separation. Children most at risk are those bereaved at three to five years and in early adolescence. Depressive and phobic disorders are the most common consequences (Black 1978). Clinical experience indicates that children can and should be helped to express grief (Wessel 1978).

(III) CHILD-REARING PRACTICES

Characteristics of child-rearing vary considerably. Parents may be overprotective or rejecting, consistent or inconsistent, active and involved, or withdrawn and passive, disciplinarian and punitive, or indifferent and lax. No one method of child-rearing or discipline is known to be correct or better than any other. However, effectiveness depends upon many factors: (i) rewards and punishments should be immediate, (ii) disciplinary demands should be reasonable and consistent, (iii) the better the parent-child relationship the more positive is the child's responses to the parent, and (iv) praise should outweigh punishment. Whenever a child does anything that pleases the parent or is appropriate and acceptable, he should be praised, whereas it is often better to ignore rather than punish naughty or disturbed behaviour as these often have an attention-seeking element. So long as the emphasis is on positive responses to positive behaviour there should be few problems and little need for attention-seeking (and anti-social) behaviour. Anti-social behaviour disturbances often follow adverse parental attitudes and inconsistent discipline (Rutter 1976: 90).

As important as discipline is the degree of independence children are allowed. A frequently suspected cause of childhood emotional problems is maternal overprotectiveness. This view has originated from Levy's frequently quoted study (1943). He found that children subjected to marked overprotection had poor peer relationships and difficulty in separation and adjustment to new situations. Later studies have confirmed that childhood emotional disturbance is significantly associated with parental overprotectiveness.

Immature and dependent parents produce unhappy children, because they depend upon the children to fulfil their own needs. The children of depressed parents, deprived of necessary life-experiences, are likely to be deprived and disturbed themselves.

(iv) THE PROVISION OF LIFE-EXPERIENCES

The child's satisfactory intellectual, emotional and social development is dependent upon the provision of appropriate life-experiences. Children need to be loved, cuddled, played with, talked to, and given the opportunity to socialize, separate, and learn. The lack of any of these is likely to impede development. The child who is not spoken to cannot learn to understand or speak and he becomes isolated and withdrawn. The child who is not cuddled and loved cannot form emotional bonds, and is unable to socialize or learn. The child deprived of the opportunity to separate from parents and mix with other children will not be able to do these when the need arises, for example, at the age of 5 when school starts.

(v) COMMUNICATION PATTERNS

Communication skills are an essential feature in the development of personality and socialization. Parents model methods of expressing thoughts and feelings for their children. The child's ability to communicate freely and accurately is determined by the parental ability to teach the child those skills. Children need to be given the labels for what they think and how they feel, and given permission to express thoughts and feelings.

A major feature of pathological family function is the distortion of communication (pp. 96–7). There may be ambiguity or vagueness, excess or persistence in what is said; disregard or contradiction by those who are spoken to. A child's feelings may be ignored, denied, devalued, or contradicted. Children may learn to withhold their feelings for fear of the consequences.

(vi) FAMILY COMPOSITION

It has been found that children from large families (four or more children) have a higher incidence of educational under-achievement, intellectual impairment and delinquency, when matched with children from small families, when all other variables are equal (Rutter and Madge 1976). The most likely explanations are that in large families the parents have less time to spend with each child and so may provide less stimulation and education. Further, large families tend to be more disorganized, and so both verbal interchange and discipline could be inconsistent and confused. Finally, discord and disharmony in large families are more likely. It is not surprising therefore that children from such families are likely to have more problems. However, many children from large families do succeed and cope well in life, so that family size in itself may not be as important as the ability of the parents to cope with all the demands.

Another point of interest is that the eldest child, whatever size the family, is more at risk of experiencing emotional disorders. Probable explanations for this phenomenon are that the parents of a first child are less experienced and so likely to make more mistakes, and that this child has the additional stress of coping with the arrival of siblings, and thus losing his place as favoured child. Further, parental anxiety is likely to be less with succeeding children than with the first.

(VII) MATERNAL EMPLOYMENT

Contrary to some expectations, there is in general no evidence to show that the children of working mothers have a higher incidence of emotional or behaviour disorders (Pilling and Kellmer Pringle 1978). Determining factors include the quality and consistency of the substitute care, especially in early life, and the mother's attitude to working. The more positive her attitude, the less damaging is this for the child. It is even suggested that a little time away from his mother may be beneficial for the child, and that mothers who work have a lower incidence of, and a quicker recovery from, episodes of depression (Mostow and Newberry 1975).

(VIII) PARENTAL DISTURBANCE

The most common problems in this category are maternal depression and parental anti-social personality disorders. Depressed mothers have more children with a wide range of behavioural and emotional problems and anti-social fathers have more children with anti-social behaviour disorders (Graham 1977). The mother is unable to respond to her child's needs, and the father both models anti-social behaviour and is a central figure in family discord and disorganization.

(IX) ONE-PARENT FAMILIES

The most common reasons for children to be living with only one parent are illegitimacy, separation or divorce, and death of one parent. Clearly, each of these is likely to increase the risk of disturbance in the child, probably through a combination of factors. A single parent receives less emotional and practical support, there is a greater chance of financial hardship, and there is likely to be considerable emotional trauma surrounding any loss that has occurred. The child lacks the modelling experience of two adults relating, and if the same-sexed parent is missing, the child misses the sex-role identification. It has been suggested, however, that the fact of having only one parent is less important than the quality of parenting provided, and the emotional climate and social circumstances of the home (Rutter 1976).

(X) ADOPTION

Between 2–3 per cent of all infants born in the United Kingdom are adopted, i.e. about 22,000 per annum. It is difficult to assess the effect of adoption *per se* on a child, for that child may well have experienced a variety of placements and traumas prior to the adoption. One of the most helpful reviews of adopted children is that written by Wolff (1974). Amongst other studies, she describes the comparison of illegitimate adopted and illegitimate non-adopted children. The non-adopted children had a far higher rate of psychiatric disorder and educational failure than the adopted group. Indeed, in comparison with children in the general community, adopted children have only a slightly higher incidence of psychiatric disturbance and of poor educational attainment. This is more marked in boys.

It is probable that one of the most important factors is the adoption procedure itself. Wolff suggests that mothers of illegitimate children would be more encouraged to opt for adoption by early direct placement of the child. She claims that early adoption

promotes a more successful outcome. She recommends that pro-
spective adoptive parents shoud have a full medical and psychiatric
examination 'so that adopted children will go to parents free from
psychiatric illness and personality disorder, who will survive and
whose marriage will last until the child grows up' (p. 170).

(XI)   CYCLE OF DEPRIVATION

Undoubtedly many childhood disorders are the result of disadvantages in the child's experience within the family and in general social
and physical conditions. Privation and maladjustment can be trans-
mitted from one generation to the next. Because they have lacked
appropriate and satisfying experiences within their own family of
origin, parents may be unable to provide adequate experiences for
their own children. We point out later that poor quality housing,
schools, and child care provision have been shown to contribute
towards a child's disturbance and it is easy to see how the continuation of these kinds of privation and disadvantage contribute to a
cycle of deprivation. A most comprehensive example of this cycle
spanning four generations has recently been described (Oliver and
Buchanan 1979).

Socio-cultural factors

It is likely that socio-economic and cultural factors play an important
part in the genesis of childhood problems. It is very difficult to
determine the relative contribution of each variable, not least because
of the interaction between them. We discuss in this section those
factors that we consider to be of most importance, though not in any
specific order.

(I)   POVERTY

Poverty is likely to be associated with other socio-cultural factors
such as poor housing and unemployment, family factors such as
increased tension and disharmony, and such biological factors as
poor nutrition, inadequate antenatal care, and increased suscepti-
bility to disease. Yet by no means all children from poor homes
manifest disorders relating to physical or psychological development,

and in contrast many children from financially comfortable families need help for a variety of emotional, behavioural, and developmental problems. As it is impossible to isolate poverty as a variable in any studies its exact contribution cannot be specified, but it is likely to be of major importance.

(II)   URBAN VERSUS RURAL LIFE

There is a higher rate of behaviour problems in urban as opposed to rural children (Rutter *et al.* 1976). In studies comparing 10–11 year-olds in an Inner London Borough and on the Isle of Wight the incidence of all common types of childhood disturbance (and specific reading retardation) is twice as high in the urban setting. The reasons are not completely clear but it is suggested that the disturbance is mediated not through the direct effect of urban problems but through distorted family relationships. Family disruption and distortion are undoubtedly higher in urban areas, and 'if some way could be found to protect the family from undesirable urban influences any directly adverse effect of the urban environment on the child would be negligible' (Graham 1977: 23). These findings may not apply in underdeveloped countries where, for example, the quality of rural life is poorer.

(III)   HOUSING STATUS

In recent years much concern has been expressed about the effects of living in certain types of housing, e.g. high-rise flats (Richman 1974). However, the results of studies into the psychiatric consequences of living in blocks of flats are somewhat contradictory, e.g. compare Moore (1974) and Richman (1974). It is probable that the *quality* of housing is of more relevance than the *type* in contributing to adult illness and childhood behaviour problems. Thus, it matters less whether the family live in a flat or house, and more that the home is in good repair, uncramped, warm, and dry. Pollak (1979) reports in her study on the effect of housing on developmental level of 3 year-old children that the quality of housing did not significantly affect developmental level.

(IV) IMMIGRANT STATUS

In general, immigrants have a higher rate of childhood psychiatric disorder, though in this country this excess is restricted to West Indian children who have a higher incidence of anti-social behaviour disorders. Contributory factors to this phenomenon include family disruption, large family size, poor housing, poor child-minding, prejudice, and discrimination (Rutter *et al.* 1975).

(V) EFFECT OF SCHOOLS

Although the influence of the home is greater than that of the school (Barnes and Lucas 1974) the effect the school has on the child's development should not be underestimated. In a massive study of 16 secondary schools in an Inner London Borough, Rutter and his colleagues (1979) made the following points. There is a marked variation between schools in children's behaviour and attainment. When all else is equal (e.g. background of children, staff-pupil ratio, etc.) some schools achieve far more than others. In contrast to housing, the size of the school, the age of the building, and the space available are not relevant. The schools that have positive influences on the children have a degree of emphasis on academic achievement, provide good conditions for the pupils, make available incentives and rewards, provide responsibility for the children, and encourage a high degree of teacher involvement in the lessons. Schools lacking these features have a negative effect on the children. The cumulative effect of these various social factors is greater than the effect of any individual factors.

The authors conclude that to a considerable extent, children's behaviour and attitudes are shaped and influenced by school experiences, and in particular by the qualities of the school as a social institution. The results carry the strong implication that schools can do much to foster good behaviour and attainments, and that even in a disadvantaged area schools can be a force for the good.

(VI) PEER GROUPS

Although it is generally accepted that the peer group can act as a powerful influence upon behaviour especially during adolescence, there is no evidence that the peer group can in its own right be primarily harmful. Coleman (1979: 185) in a discussion of anti-social behaviour in adolescence comments that 'peer group influence can only be exercised under certain circumstances, and in particular where the parents leave a vacuum by showing little concern or interest, or where they themselves provide a model for anti-social behaviour'. Although adolescent drinking and anti-social behaviour both tend to occur in the presence of peers, many researchers have shown that drinking begins in the family setting (e.g. Aitken 1978) and that delinquents frequently have a family history of criminality (e.g. West 1974).

(vii) LABELLING

It has been argued that labelling serves as a self-fulfilling prophecy, with, for example, delinquents, so-labelled, being more likely to commit delinquent acts. Labelling theory is easy to state but validation by research is enormously difficult. There is evidence that in some circumstances the effect exists (Rutter and Madge 1976) but an opposite beneficial effect can also occur; for example, teachers may respond positively to children labelled as low achievers (Brophy and Good 1974). It is also possible that a label may have no effect.

Biological factors

(i) GENETIC

Genetic factors play an important role in the determination of individual differences in intelligence, temperament, personality variation, and emotional disorders (Shields 1973). However, the genetic contribution cannot be considered in isolation. There is an interaction between the genetic endowment and the environment which determines the final picture. A child may be born with the potential for high intelligence but if deprived of stimulus and affection this capacity will not be realized.

Both genes and chromosomes can have fundamental mutations or defects. Gene mutations may give rise to a wide number of inherited diseases. Chromosomal defects are the cause of a variety of abnormalities of physical appearance, sexual development, or intellect.

Examples include Down's Syndrome (Mongolism) and Turner's Syndrome, in which the girls are small and infertile.

(ii) PRENATAL

It has been well established that adverse influences during pregnancy may cause impaired development after birth. Undoubtedly the developing foetus may be damaged by maternal infection by rubella (German measles), syphilis, and a number of viruses. A wide range of drugs including the nicotine in cigarettes can have a similar effect. Other adverse prenatal influences include toxaemia of pregnancy (pre-eclamptic toxaemia or PET) and maternal illness. Any of these factors may be responsible for less obvious damage such as low birth-weight. There is no evidence that isolated stresses *per se* during the pregnancy affect the foetus, but it has been reported that severe continuing personal tensions (especially marital discord) during pregnancy are closely associated with childhood ill-health, developmental delay, and behaviour disturbances (Stott 1973).

(iii) PERINATAL

A lack of oxygen (anoxia) during birth, excessive use of drugs during labour, or premature delivery, may predispose to brain damage and neuropsychiatric disorders. Some of these problems are described under the heading of 'minimal brain dysfunction' (pp. 78–9).

(iv) POST-NATAL

The neonate, being so vulnerable, is exposed to a variety of problems. A frequent complication in the first week of life is neonatal jaundice which has various causes. Most types are relatively harmless, but the jaundice due to blood group incompatibility (including rhesus and ABO) may cause brain damage if not correctly treated. Other possible post-natal causes of brain damage include trauma, infections, and under nutrition.

(v) PHYSICAL

Psychiatric problems and developmental disorders may have their origins in physical disease or injury. Brain damage or dysfunction with all its sequelae can result from trauma, infection, biochemical disorders, and other serious illnesses. Recurrent or prolonged physical illness or handicap which does not directly affect the brain may none the less produce emotional, behavioural, or learning problems, due to the anxieties they may arouse, the different life-style imposed upon the child, and the interruptions in social and educational development. In a comprehensive epidemiological study carried out on the Isle of Wight it was found that emotional or behaviour problems occurred in 7 per cent of physically normal children, 12 per cent of children with non-neurological illnesses, and 35 per cent of children with neurological disorders (Rutter, Tizard, and Whitmore 1970).

(vi) SEX DIFFERENCES

The majority of psychological problems of childhood are more common in boys, for example, developmental delays, enuresis, and anti-social behaviour problems, although emotional problems such as fears or school-refusal affect the sexes equally. There is no clear explanation for these differences although it has been suggested that cerebral maturation is more rapid in girls, possibly accounting for a lower incidence of developmental delay. There is no evidence that social factors such as differences in child-rearing are of relevance.

(vii) TEMPERAMENTAL CHARACTERISTICS

Temperament is a general term used to describe characteristics of behavioural individuality identified in infancy and early childhood – it concerns the way in which an individual behaves, and describes the *how* rather than the *what* (content) or *why* (explanation) of behaviour (Thomas and Chess 1977). Temperamental characteristics include activity level, rhythmicity, adaptability, intensity of reaction, irritability, quality of mood, distractability, fastidiousness, and withdrawal. Individuals may be described as high, medium, or low on most of these characteristics.

Temperamental characteristics are predominantly genetically-determined, with parental attitudes and functioning having only a minimal influence, and they are well established by the age of 2–3 months. However, temperament does not follow a consistent linear development, for it may be modified by environmental influences (Thomas and Chess 1977).

There is no doubt that adverse temperamental characteristics may contribute to childhood problems by rendering the child more vulnerable to family or environmental stress (Anthony 1970, Graham, Rutter, and George 1973). Specific characteristics considered to predispose children to problems include irritability, under and overactivity, poor adaptability, tendency to withdrawal, irregularity of sleeping, eating, toileting, and low fastidiousness. Graham and his colleagues comment that

> 'the child requires handling geared to his individuality if he is to stand the best chance of avoiding the development of psychiatric disorder. Young children respond individually and there is no one role to suit them all. This may help explain why some children behave well at home and not at school, or *vice versa*. The expectations in one setting may differ dramatically from those in another, with one set being appropriate for the child, and the other quite inappropriate.'   (Graham, Rutter, and George 1973: 338)

It is important to emphasize that children's emotional and behavioural disturbances are not necessarily the direct result of maternal pathology (Thomas and Chess 1977). This is a valuable starting-point in discussing children's problems with the parents, who often have deep feelings of guilt and inadequacy as a result of needing help.

Conclusions

It is clear that psycho-social development is affected by many factors including temperamental attributes, biological and genetic influences, socio-cultural considerations and experiences relating to the family, separation, and loss.

Kellmer Pringle (1974a) has identified five groups of children in this country who have a much higher than average chance of being damaged in their development because of personal, family or social circumstances: (1) Children in large families with low incomes and living in poor houses. (2) Those children who grow up in one-parent families. (3) Those who live separate from their parents. (4) Children who suffer from a mental or physical handicap. (5) Children whose parents are mentally handicapped, socially deviant, or emotionally damaged.

We consider that as well as singling out important individual factors such as those just summarized, it is essential to consider the interaction between factors, whether they be disadvantage or dysfunction, biological or environmental, extra or intrafamilial.

The rest of this book is devoted to the means available for the assessment of children with emotional, behavioural, and developmental problems, a description of the way in which such problems are manifested, and how they may be overcome.

3

Assessment

Introduction

Before a particular intervention can be decided upon, it is essential to make a detailed assessment. Often a crisis can be cooled down without doing this but the same family will probably reappear on another occasion with yet another crisis. Although the information contained in a referral is important, it may tell us very little about the true nature of the problem, and its contents will be greatly influenced by the characteristics of the referral agent.

There is a growing awareness that the most informative way to begin an assessment is to examine the *whole* family, its structure and interaction, and we discuss in some detail the techniques for doing this. It may be necessary to assess individual members of the family, either because a family assessment has not proved possible, or further individual assessment has been indicated after seeing the family. We discuss techniques of individual assessment including psychological assessment. A third dimension requiring consideration is the family in relation to other groups and institutions within society, including the school and neighbourhood, and an assessment of any social stress, such as poor housing.

Because the core of the assessment is the family, it is a suitable model for social workers in any agency. A specialist clinic will have easier access to doctors or psychologists, but if such access is necessary, a local authority social worker could make arrangements either through the school psychological service, school health service, or local clinic.

For very many years there has been a tendency for childhood problems to be conceptualized within a medical model. In assessing medical problems, the doctor takes a detailed history of the problem, examines the patient, and then requests specific tests carried out by pathologists or radiologists. So, in child psychiatry, the psychiatrist, true to his training, obtains an history from the parent, examines the mental state of the child, and then requests specific tests such as intelligence or projective tests to be carried out by a psychologist. In management, the doctor makes a diagnosis and prescribes a treatment, and so the psychiatrist has done the same.

This medical model, also often used by social workers, presupposes a simple disease process which can be treated by a particular method, for example, a child's depression would be alleviated by anti-depressants; behaviour disturbance would be overcome after a few months of psychotherapy. Clearly, in childhood disturbance the problems are complex and the solutions far from obvious. The factors that maintain a problem may differ from those that have caused it, and in planning interventions the sorts of goals aimed for are diverse. One characteristic of this approach in the child psychiatric clinic has been the splitting of the assessment into three parts: the psychiatrist seeing the child, the social worker taking a family history from the parents, and the psychologist carrying out psychological testing. This splitting is of uncertain value, uneconomical, and time consuming.

Any well trained psychiatrist, psychologist, or social worker should be able to obtain an appropriate history and discuss a child's problems with him. Only the intellectual assessment or projective testing requires additional training currently available only for the psychologist. In the majority of cases, one well trained professional should be sufficient.

The fact that the parents are interviewed separately may reduce the child's confidence in the agency staff, feeling that his parents are complaining about him, and that other adults are bound to side with them. Similarly, the parents may feel that the staff are siding with the child.

Interviewing different members of the family separately is a denial of the wholeness of the family, and prevents the interviewer from obtaining objective information about family relationships, interaction patterns, and the role of the 'problem child' in the family.

Finally, a separate interview with the child may collude with, and therefore reinforce, his role as symptom, or carrier, of family problems. (Recognition of the wholeness of the family in no way denies individuality – see Chapter 5.)

For these reasons it has become increasingly popular to assess the whole family rather than the child alone. More often than not, it becomes clear very quickly that the family does indeed have problems, and frequently more than one child is, or should be, a cause for concern. A detailed factual account of the referred child's development and problems may still be obtained, either in the family group, or, if indicated, on a separate and later occasion. If other special investigations such as intellectual assessments are required, these may also be arranged for another time.

From the preceding chapter, it can be seen that the causes of childhood disturbance may be from within the child, reactive to the environment, or an interaction of the two. Unfortunately, in the traditional method of assessment considerable emphasis is placed on biological and developmental factors, but far less on the environment and particularly the family. Indeed, the family as a whole group is rarely seen in the majority of agencies using the traditional approach.

Cox and Rutter (1976: 290), in their review of the literature on diagnostic appraisal and interviewing, conclude that it is 'desirable to see the family both together and separately'. We choose to meet the whole family at the first interview so that the presenting problems may be viewed in the context most relevant to the child, i.e. the family and its relationships. The objections that a whole-family interview precludes the possibility of obtaining a detailed background history, or prevents parents from fully expressing their concerns are dealt with by arranging separate interviews and, indeed, special investigations, at a later date, if such information is required. An initial family assessment allows for a far more comprehensive picture to be obtained than any amount of history-taking.

Family assessment

There is a wide variety of techniques for assessing and helping families. The theories relating to these are discussed more fully in Chapter 5. We agree with Walrond-Skinner (1976: 12) that the most helpful theoretical model is that of general systems theory. This considers that a system is a whole and that its components and their characteristics can only be understood as functions of the total system. Applying this view to the family group, we can state that 'a family is a whole, and its members and their behaviour and feelings can only be understood as functions of the whole family.' Walrond-Skinner uses the game of chess as an analogy:

> 'It would not be possible to gain much understanding of chess, simply by looking at the pieces; one would need to examine the game as a whole, and to take note of how the movement of one piece affects the position and meaning of every other piece on the board.'

Family assessment may be considered in five stages:

(i) PREPARATION

Prior to the initial assessment, the whole family should be invited to attend. (Home-visiting is discussed on p. 36.) We recommend sending a letter acknowledging the concerns about the child, and stating that it is most helpful to meet all the family in the first instance. We advise them to allow a couple of hours for this appointment.

The interview room should be large enough to accommodate everyone comfortably, there should be age-appropriate drawing or play-material for the children, and the interviewer should ensure he can see everyone, preferably by arranging the chairs in a circle. A careful and determined preparation along these lines will ensure a more useful assessment.

(ii) INTRODUCTION AND ENGAGEMENT

In this phase, we introduce ourselves to the family, discuss with them the use of any special facilities such as one-way screens, video or audio equipment, and outline the aims and structure of the interview. We ask the family to introduce themselves, greeting each member personally, noting name and age, and sharing a neutral exchange. Having 'met' each family member in this way, we ascertain the family's concerns. This may be done by asking the parents initially to tell us about their problems, or by putting an open question to the whole family, so that anyone might answer, e.g. 'Who would like to start?', or 'Would you like to tell me about your difficulties?'. Each person's view is sought on any problem mentioned, and on what attempts have been made to solve the problem. In this way, we are acknowledging each family member's importance.

Some family therapists prefer to be less symptom-focused. They might start the interview by making comments on family interaction or even commenting on similarity of appearance as a way of initiating interaction. At some point it is useful to obtain details of any significant events in the life of the family, and families of origin. This may be done by obtaining a conventional social history, or asking the family to draw out their family tree, or eliciting a year-chart (i.e. a year-by-year chronicle of significant events), and this certainly provides an animated forum for observation of family interaction. Children are usually pleased to be involved, and often surprise their parents with their knowledge, interest, and occasionally their ignorance. Such activities draw families together and help them to relax and lose some of their anxiety.

(III) FAMILY DESCRIPTION

It is as important to be aware of patterns of family interaction and the quality of family relationships as it is to know about the family background. An effective way of observing and understanding these family processes is to study the detail of the presenting problem and the interaction around it. We elicit the nature of the problem, when it started, the effect it has had on each family member, what attempts have been made to modify it, and with what results. As the family deals with these questions, a pattern of relationships, and repetitive sequences of behaviour emerge. If certain members of the family remain silent, their non-verbal behaviour is in itself a statement about their unwillingness, or inability, to participate. However, they may be encouraged to participate, directly by the interviewer, who seeks their view on what has been said, or by the interviewer asking the more verbal family members to involve the less verbal ones. The seating arrangements of the family also provide useful information about relationships.

Young children may be engaged by play and drawings. Dare and

Lindsay (1979) have given a most helpful description of the involvement of young children in family assessment and therapy. They emphasize the importance of showing interest in the children by greeting them individually, and responding personally to their verbal and non-verbal contributions. They insist on using language that may be understood by any young children in the family, and ask children to stop them if they do not understand. They use the children's play-material to make direct contact with the children themselves.

Once the family has started describing the problems, we note the various aspects of their interactional patterns. It is helpful to consider these under five headings.

(a) Atmosphere. This refers to the overall mood of the family, happy, sad, angry, tense, etc. In addition, we note the range of emotions evident, their intensity, how they are communicated, and how they are handled; what feelings are tolerated, what feelings are denied or mocked. Who conveys what feelings to whom?

(b) Structural relationships. This term derives from the structural theory of family therapy. The structuralists, of whom Minuchin and his colleagues in Philadelphia are the most well-known, consider the family as a system that operates through various transactional patterns, for example, how, when, and who relates to whom? The family system differentiates and carries out its function through various sub-systems, for example, the parental sub-system, the sibling sub-system, the father-son sub-system, etc. (A sub-system consists of one or more individuals formed by generation, sex, interest, or function.) The structural family therapist is concerned with the cohesiveness and adaptability of the family and its sub-systems (Minuchin 1974). Structural theory and its practical application are discussed in detail in Chapter 5. An attempt should be made by the interviewer to describe the family in these terms.

(c) Family tasks. Families have various tasks (see p. 12) and this heading refers to the ability of the family to complete these tasks. How well are the parents able to fulfil their functions? Which parent does what? Can they assist their children to cope with the various developmental phases and transitions, for example, separation,

arrival of a new-born sibling, schooling, puberty, leaving home? How do the family make decisions, solve problems, and resolve conflict? Are conflicts left unresolved, or are they denied, or detoured through third persons?

(d) Communication. Communication is both verbal and non-verbal. The family therapist is interested in both the quality and quantity of communication (see Chapter 5). He looks for clarity and continuity. He notes who is the family spokesman, who speaks to whom, who is allowed to say what, and who is allowed to interrupt. He considers the meaning of non-verbal communications and is aware of the contradictions between the non-verbal and verbal elements of a communication.

(e) Therapist involvement. In the same way as a psychotherapist is aware of his feelings about his client (the countertransference) so the family therapist should be aware of his reaction to the family, his feelings, their range and intensity, his degree of activity, etc. Feelings that arise during the course of the interview (as opposed to those brought into it) are likely to be a response to the family interaction. The therapist is often made to feel the same way as some of the family members (for example, the children).

(IV) FORMULATION

Having spent an hour or so with the family, the interviewer should leave them so that he may have some time to collect his thoughts. He needs to find answers to the following questions:
  (a) What is happening?
  (b) What is maintaining it?
  (c) How may it have arisen?
  (d) What attempts at change have been made and with what effect?
  (e) What would constitute desirable change?
  (f) How might this be achieved?
   It may not be possible at this stage to answer all the questions, but an attempt should nonetheless be made to write down a clear statement answering them as fully as possible. This phase of formulation is an essential prerequisite for successful intervention. It is

perfectly legitimate to request a further interview to obtain more information, and particularly so if a key family member has failed to attend. The interviewer can say to the family, 'Please could you tell . . . . . that I feel uncomfortable discussing people behind their backs, and as he is so obviously important to you all, I think it would be most helpful if he could come next time.'

The experienced family therapist prepares an initial formulation during the first meeting. However, he recognizes that as he gains more knowledge of the family, and indeed as the family begins to change, so the formulation will alter. We agree with other family therapists who consider that assessment and treatment merge, starting with the first contact with the family, and assessment only stopping when therapy ceases.

We have included a sample formulation to illustrate some of the points made in this section.

Sample family formulation

The Davis family consists of father, aged 48, an engineer, mother, aged 46, who used to teach before having children, Eileen, 21, at university, Helen, 18, taking A-levels, and Jean, aged 15, the referred child. The presenting problems are Jean's truancy, staying out late, and disobedience. The parents present a united front in their concern about Jean, who is herself supported by Eileen, who accuses her parents of being over-concerned and over-intrusive. Helen is seen by her parents as the daughter who can do no wrong. Covert conflict between the parents is exploited by Eileen who points out their disagreements over their expectations of Jean. Her persistent criticisms seemingly unite them in a joint attack on both her and Jean. The therapist's comments on this repetitive pattern lead to an opening-up of the marital disagreement, and a realignment of family relationships. Mother and Helen move closer, isolating father, on one side, and confronting Jean and Eileen on the other.

The family have consistently denied any problem other than Jean's and the only attempts to change have been the introduction of increasingly punitive measures against her. The marital conflict has been denied and avoided. Father particularly distances himself from the family. Conflict is diverted onto Jean, whose behaviour may be an expression of her distressing role, and Eileen, whose criticisms help the parents unite against her.

For change to occur, the parents would have to acknowledge and confront their own difficulties, and Eileen would have to allow them to do this without diverting them. This may best be achieved by a series of meetings with the parents alone, with the occasional meeting for the whole family to consolidate such change. The outlook at this stage is uncertain because the depth of the marital disturbance is not yet known. They do, however, appear keen for help.

(v) FUTURE PLANNING

The interviewer shares with the family as much of his formulation as he considers to be appropriate, so offering them a partnership in attempting to resolve the problems. He advises them of his views about the most appropriate way of helping. He may consider it necessary to have further meetings to clarify areas of uncertainty or to arrange for additional information to be obtained, for example, a school report, an intellectual assessment, or a report from another agency. He may wish to discuss the family with a colleague or supervisor before deciding on the next step. In any of these instances he should explain this to the family and make a further appointment.

If the interviewer is confident of his formulation and clear about the aims, he should discuss them with the family and offer further help. He may decide that a series of family meetings is indicated in which case he should negotiate a *contract* with the family, or specified members of it, for a specific number of meetings on a regular basis, with predetermined and clearly-stated aims (see Chapter 5).

Alternatively, he may consider it more appropriate for one person alone to be seen, or for just the parents to attend. There are many styles of intervention (see Chapters 5–11) and a variety of factors will determine which of these is used. Important considerations in this respect include the therapist's training and conceptual framework, agency resources, time available, effects of previous interventions, client motivation, and the results of treatment outcome research. Whatever management plan is devised, it should be discussed with the family, the rationale and aims being clearly outlined.

In *Table 3(1)* we have outlined an *aide-memoire* for family assessment, which can be used in conjunction with the preceding description.

Table 3(1) Aide-memoire for family assessment

---

(1) Family Composition
(2) Presenting Problems
(3) Salient Features of Family Background
(4) Family Description
    (a) Atmosphere
    (b) Structure
    (c) Tasks
    (d) Communication
    (e) Therapist involvement
(5) Formulation
(6) Management

FAMILY ASSESSMENT AT HOME

A family assessment can be carried out just as well at home as in a particular agency, indeed one could argue that there is opportunity to gain more information about home circumstances and neighbourhood characteristics and that the family may be more relaxed. However, many workers feel less in control in a family's own home, and Lindsey (1979) in her detailed discussion of home assessment stresses the need to resolve the conflict around the issue of authority.

> 'It is necessary to be able to take charge of the household. A generous acknowledgement of the family's sense of intrusion into their privacy is helpful. At the same time, the worker must convey a sufficient sense of confidence in his expertise and respect for the importance to the family of his task with them to enable them to take it seriously.'   (p. 119)

She also emphasizes the importance of the whole family attending, and not starting until everyone is seated, the television is switched off, and the interviewer is able to see everyone.

DISCUSSION

We do not dispute that to arrange a meeting with a whole family, to learn about their background, observe the full richness of their relationships, understand the problems, decide upon interventions and carry them out, is a daunting task. Many reservations have been expressed about the family approach; it is uneconomical and time-consuming; it is not possible to find out about the referred child, to understand his inner conflicts and to help him deal with these; it is harmful to the children to hear their parents' criticisms of them or, indeed, of each other; the parents will not be able to talk in front of the children, and *vice versa*.

The criticism of the family approach being uneconomical can only be based on cost-effectiveness. As yet, no one has studied this; however, there is a large number of studies of family therapy outcome, indicating its effectiveness as an intervention (e.g. Gurman and Kniskern 1979). We shall discuss these further in Chapter 5 on family therapy, but at this stage it is worth stating that there are virtually no studies demonstrating the effectiveness of *individual* forms of therapy, other than the behavioural approaches.

In agencies such as social services departments where referrals may not be for a formal assessment but rather to deal with one particular difficulty, for example, a child briefly running away from home, or stealing from mother's purse, a family assessment should still be made. It may be that no further work is to be done with the family at that point, but it is so easy for families to be seen on repeated occasions by different workers for various problems, with no one ever really understanding what is going on.

A paediatrician (Weller 1975) has commented that:

> 'By failing to see the whole family as a collective patient, we run the risk of adding to the burden on the community. Not only may the child have to be re-admitted but the damage to the family may mean more calls on the general practitioner and social services, both now and in the future, as the stresses wreak havoc on the personalities of the next generation.'   (p. 36)

Certainly, a family assessment takes time, but probably less than that involved in individual assessment. The family interviewer may spend two hours with the family, in contrast to, for example, the psychiatrist spending an hour with the child, the social worker one or two hours with the parents, and the case conference for sharing of information taking at least another half an hour.

Dare and Lindsey (1979) have described very clearly how an understanding of the child's inner conflicts may be gained in family interviews. Indeed, the more psychoanalytically-oriented family therapists concentrate all their endeavours on this focus, often neglecting the complexities of the family as a system.

Whether or not it is really harmful for a child to hear parental criticism and conflict during family interviews, the fact is that he is exposed to this at home. It seems far more helpful if the interviewer is able to observe the full range, quality, and intensity of negative affect and communications within the family setting. In this way, he can note the sequences of events that lead up to the behaviour complained of, the reaction of the child to the criticisms, and the way in which the 'problem-behaviour' is handled.

In later sessions, the parents may request, or the therapist suggest, separate interviews for the discussion of sexual or other personal difficulties. Churven (1978) has reported a study of parental attitudes to family assessment. He found that twenty out of twenty-five families were willing to participate in whole-family assessment. He added that those unable to attend the clinic would co-operate in the home setting, out of working-hours.

For a more detailed account of family interviewing see Minuchin (1974) and Satir (1978: 91–173).

The family and the outside world

Just as a child cannot be understood in isolation from his family, so a family cannot be understood in isolation from the society in which it lives. A consideration of the family in relation to the outside world adds another necessary dimension to the initial assessment.

The child and his school

It has been common practice in specialist clinics to obtain a report from the referred child's school. It may also be useful to obtain information concerning his siblings' functioning in school. This information should include estimation of the child's adjustment, relationships, behaviour, and abilities from the teacher(s) who knows him best. Behaviour may well vary between home and school (see Chapter 2) and, if so, this should be noted. It is fairly easy to outline the kinds of information that would be useful in a particular case, but it is not always easy to collect it. Many clinics send out a standardized questionnaire to the school of every child concerned, and the one in common use is that produced by Rutter (1967). The use of such a questionnaire not only provides some guidelines for the teacher about the information required, but also allows for a rough prediction of the seriousness of the problem. The use of a questionnaire, coupled with a direct discussion with teachers is the best form of assessment. Possible school-based aetiological factors are discussed in Chapter 2, and issues related to working with schools are discussed in Chapter 9. It is clearly very important to build up good relationships with schools and to be aware of their criteria for concern. One school we know wanted to expel a child for a mischievous prank, while another tolerated a pupil setting fire to the school on more than one occasion.

When asking for permission to contact the school, the parents may express concern about the spread of information and the possibility that perhaps their child may be stigmatized for the whole of his school career. It is important to stress to parents that we would be asking *for* information, and not actually conveying any details of our own assessment *to* the school. Such a commitment to confidentiality may go some way to allaying understandable anxiety.

THE FAMILY AND OTHER GROUPS IN SOCIETY

The social worker is well used to making this type of assessment, and it is not necessary to enter into great detail here. Unfortunately, the traditional child guidance approach has tended to neglect social factors. The aims of this aspect of assessments are: (1) to discover any problems that are not already known, e.g. that the family is unable to make relationships with any of the neighbours; (2) to assess the ways in which society has failed the family, and the subsequent stresses, e.g. bad housing, neighbourhood decay, racial disharmony, un-employment; (3) to obtain information about how the resources in society might be used in any interventions, e.g. a suitable playgroup for the active child of a depressed mother.

Pincus and Minahan (1973) provide a helpful framework in which to consider a child's problem that fully incorporates this aspect of the assessment. They outline three different resource systems: (1) informal or natural resource systems, e.g. family and neighbourhood; (2) formal resource systems, e.g. clubs and societies; (3) formal institutions, such as schools and hospitals. Pincus and Minahan advocate that one should look at ways in which these resource systems are failing a particular client. There are myriad ways in which these may be failing, for instance, a neighbourhood may be unable to accept the unusual behaviour of a schizophrenic mother, or the police might be harassing a young black teenager, thus exacerbating his anti-social behaviour. Indeed, such negative discrimination can be found throughout society. A client may also be unaware of the existence of certain resource systems or lack the skills in dealing with others, e.g. Department of Health and Social Security.

As a background to the assessment of the family in relation to the outside world, it is useful to have a good knowledge of the local communities, schools, and clubs. Many departments build up their own resource files in which information can be stored. Other local social workers or community workers could be called upon to fill any gaps in information. Each family provides considerable information, but as well as asking for a school assessment, it is often useful to obtain the family's permission to contact other professionals, e.g. health visitors, general practitioners, and other social workers or club leaders to obtain further information about family members. This should not be done without their permission.

Child assessment

There are times when it is necessary to interview the child alone, and make an individual assessment. Such instances might include those times when the family, or key members, refuse to attend, when a court or other form of individual report is required, or when mental illness in the child is suspected. In this section, we have outlined an approach to child assessment which is based on the assumption that a family assessment has not been carried out. Clearly, it is preferable to complete a family assessment as well whenever possible.

We strongly believe that the person who takes the social history from the parents, be it a psychiatrist, social worker, or psychologist, should also interview the child. Having one person, for example the social worker, take the history, and another, for example the psychiatrist, interview the child, is an anachronism based on out-moded and inaccurate ideas of comparative skills. Undoubtedly, the social worker has a particular training in assessing social back-ground, the psychiatrist is taught to examine patients, and the psychologist knows how to administer and interpret intelligence tests. However, we believe that any professional whose job involves the assessment and care of disturbed or distressed children should learn to make a comprehensive assessment for himself. The corollary to this is that the same professional should have a practical knowledge of the important methods of treatment.

Highly specific tasks will remain the prerogative of individual disciplines. Psychiatrists, for example, are responsible for physical examinations, investigations, and treatments. Psychologists admin-ister and interpret psychological tests, and it is the social worker who would apply for any necessary legislative measures. Clearly, the individuals concerned may use their team for deciding on aspects of case management and for gaining support in their therapeutic efforts.

TAKING THE HISTORY

A detailed history helps to promote an understanding of significant aetiological factors and to decide upon appropriate interventions. It should be obtained from both parents. The child's relationship with his father is as important as that with his mother, and so the father's view of the problem deserves equal consideration. It is totally un-satisfactory to rely upon the mother's account of the father's view, as this account may be distorted and influenced by many factors. Further, an interview with both parents will provide useful infor-mation on the quality of their relationship.

(a) Presenting problem. It is customary to start the history-taking by focusing on the presenting problem. Specific information is sought about when the problem started, what seems to precipitate it, what happens, how often, and when, what effects do the child's problem have on the child and the family, what influences the problem, what measures have been taken to help, what is the child's view of what is happening, how restricted is he, and how impaired is his develop-ment? Having acquired such details about the presenting problems,

it is helpful to question systematically about all aspects of the child's development, behaviour, and background.

(b) Developmental detail.   Details are sought of; (i) history of the pregnancy (planned or otherwise, interruptions, illness, medication), (ii) delivery (home or hospital, premature, postmature, induced, spontaneous, forceps, Caesarean, prolonged, precipitate, use of medication), (iii) post-natal period (state of baby after birth, neonatal behaviour, sleeping, feeding – breast or bottle, parental reactions, how long in hospital), (iv) infancy (temperament, feeding, sleeping, vomiting, colic), (v) milestones – age first smiled, sat up, crawled, stood, walked, words, phrases, use of potty, and toilet-training. Note is made of early personality characteristics and behaviour patterns, for example, ability to separate, reaction to stress, relationship to peers, siblings, and parents. Winnicott (1971b: 4) has stressed the significance of 'transitional objects' – that special object, e.g. a doll, or a rag, to which the child is especially attached and which serves as a comforter. This helps the child to make the transition from total dependence to self-reliance. It is helpful to know about the child's special objects, his relation to them, and the parental reaction to the child's attachment.

(c) Recent health and emotional state.   The next section of the interview is concerned with the child's recent health and emotional state. The parents are asked about his general health, including recent illnesses, eating and sleeping patterns, and any aches or pains, etc. Questions are asked relating to general mood, worries and fears, and temperamental characteristics (Chapter 2). It is helpful to know about any habits or mannerisms such as tics, head-banging, thumb-sucking, speech problems, and continued attachment to special objects. What are his special interests and what does he not like doing?

(d) Relationships.   A further area for exploration is that of the child's relationships with peers, siblings, parents, and other adults. Is he particularly close to anyone, does he have particular difficulty separating, is there anyone with whom he gets on badly?

(e) Behaviour difficulties.   These are often a source of concern. Is the child disobedient, defiant, or rude: does he lie or steal; has he ever set

fire to anything, or deliberately damaged objects; is he unduly aggressive, or does he have temper tantrums; has he taken drugs or alcohol, or been in trouble with the police?

(f) *School adjustment.* Information about school adjustment should be sought. What sort of school does he attend, how many schools has he been to, how does he get on at school, with work, peers, games, and the teachers?

(g) *Sexual development.* Parents should also be asked about sexual development. Has the child reached puberty, is he interested in the opposite sex, has he received sex instruction?

(h) *Family structure and history.* The next main area of exploration is the family structure and history. What are the names, ages, occupations, etc., of other members of the family, including the extended family? Have there been any developmental problems, or emotional or physical illnesses in other family members? What are the housing circumstances, and are there any financial problems?

(i) *Family life and relationships.* What is the quality of the parental relationship, do they share responsibilities and activities? Can they discuss problems together, and work out solutions? Who makes the decisions? How does each parent get on with each child? Winnicott (1971b: 10) has described the 'good-enough mother' – mothering that 'makes active adaptation to the infant's needs, an adaptation that gradually lessens, according to the infant's growing ability to account for failure of adaptation, and to tolerate the results of frustration'. He includes in this concept fathers – 'fathers must allow me to use the term "maternal" to describe the total attitude to babies and their care'. One aspect of the assessment is consideration of whether the mothering is 'good enough'.

We recognize that it may not be possible to obtain all this information, certainly in a first interview. Further, if the interviewer is determined to get answers to all the questions he may miss important verbal and non-verbal cues given by the parents. It is far more useful to let the parents provide as much information as possible in answer to each single question, rather than interrupting them because of a need to complete the questioning.

Table 3(2) provides an *aide-memoire* for history-taking when doing an individual assessment.

Table 3(2) Aide-memoire for history-taking

(a) Presenting problems	– onset, length, quality, effect, attempts to change, precipitating factors.
(b) Developmental detail	– i antenatal ii labour and delivery iii post-natal iv infancy v milestones.
(c) Recent health and emotional state	– general health, recent illnesses, eating and sleeping, symptoms, general mood, worries, etc., temperamental characteristics, habits and mannerisms.
(d) Relationships	– peers, siblings, parents, other adults.
(e) Behaviour difficulties	– disobedience, defiance, rudeness, lies or stealing, aggression, drugs, alcohol, police.
(f) School adjustment	– schools attended, quality, attainment, socialization.
(g) Sexual development	– puberty, interests, instruction.
(h) Family structure and history	– details of all members of current and extended family, and important events in life of family.
(i) Family life and relationships	– parental relationship, parent-child relationships, sibling relationships, activities, interests.

Interview with the child

Careful preparation aids assessment of a child in the same way as it does a family. The skill of talking with a child is something that can only be gained by experience and training, but the interviewer can set the scene to ease his task. He should ensure he has the use of a quiet room, equipped with play-material which is both age and sex-appropriate. Very young (pre-school) children need toys, some drawing material, and perhaps sand or water. School-age (but pre-adolescent) children are more likely to use drawing material, but a variety of toys and modelling equipment are usually appreciated. Adolescents will probably shun toys and drawing material, but it is advisable to provide something like Plasticine for them to fiddle with, thus helping them feel more comfortable. When funds are limited, a few items will suffice, for example, a dolls' house, or equivalent, with Play-people, some crayons and paper, and Plasticine or Playdoh.

Obviously, the interviewer should not be seated behind a desk. Preferably, he should arrange for a couple of chairs to be available, and a low surface for toys and drawing material. The initial and most important task is that of gaining the child's confidence so that a satisfactory rapport may be achieved. We advise that the interviewer start by showing the child round the room, and explaining the structure of the interview. It is important to use words and concepts that the child understands. For example, when stating the length of the interview to a 5 year-old, the interviewer might say, 'We will be together for about half an hour, that's as long as (a particular television programme) lasts'. The child should be told that he may play with any of the material, and the interviewer should then pause and allow him the opportunity to involve himself spontaneously in play. The interviewer may then note the content of the play (see below).

It is a mistake to start by discussing the presenting problems – the child may already be feeling under attack, and wary of further adult instructions; far better to discuss neutral topics such as the child's interest, friends, favourite toys, or television programmes. As rapport is gained, it is possible to introduce gradually some of the problems. Frequently aspects of the child's life are reproduced in his play or drawings. If, for example, the play involves a parent smacking a child, it is reasonable to say something like, 'Maybe your mummy gets cross with you sometimes and then she smacks you'. If the child agrees, the interviewer might make a sympathetic statement and encourage him to talk more about it.

When the play or drawings are not very revealing, the interviewer might make a general statement such as, 'I know a lot of boys of your age whose mothers always seem to be getting cross with them and sometimes smack them – I wonder if that happens to you?'. Or, 'I saw a little girl yesterday who told me that she gets so unhappy that she often has a little cry in bed at night – perhaps you do sometimes?'. Such statements make it permissible for a child to admit to behaviour or feelings he is ashamed of, or does not understand. This principle applies to many emotionally laden topics, for example, 'Many children get so cross with their brothers or sisters they wish they could get rid of them, and I wouldn't be surprised if you felt that sometimes, too'. In our experience, children respond honestly to such an approach, and do not agree simply to satisfy the interviewer. Asking leading questions without such facilitative statements is almost always fruitless. For example, if a child is asked 'Do you cry at night?', almost certainly he will deny it, whatever the truth. At all times, the interviewer should be gentle, empathic, non-judgmental, and facilitative.

As the interview proceeds, various aspects of the child's behaviour should be noted. These are summarized in the *aide-memoire* in *Table 3(3)*. Here we have outlined various questions that need to be answered in the description of an interview.

(a) General description of the child.   Is the child of normal size and appearance for his age; are there any abnormalities in appearance; are there any signs of bruising or ill health, etc.; what clothing does he wear; does he look well cared for; is he restless or fidgety; can he concentrate or is he distractible; does he have any strange mannerisms such as tics?

(b) Parent-child relationship.   What sort of rapport do they have; what is the quality of the relationship; how do they communicate; do they hold hands, do they cuddle; how readily does the child separate?

(c) Mood of the child.   How appropriate is the child's mood to the situation; is he sad or happy, fearful or relaxed, warm or distant; does he cry, does he laugh, does he have any specific fears?

(d) Talk and thought.   How readily does he talk; does he change the subject; are the thought processes logical; are there any bizarre thoughts; what are the child's preoccupations?

(e) Rapport.   How does the child relate to the interviewer; is he friendly or hostile; does he enquire about the interviewer's children; what effect does he have on the interviewer?

(f) Intelligence and development.   In the interviewer's judgment, is the child below or above average intelligence or within the normal range;

is he within the normal range of intellectual development for his age, i.e. has he reached the appropriate developmental milestones (see *Table 3(4)*); is his language expression and understanding age-appropriate?

(g) Play. How readily does he play; what does he do; what is the content of his play; can he play symbolically; what is the content of his drawings; does he persist?

(h) Fantasies. What would he do with three magic wishes; what does he dream about; what does he want to do when he grows up; what are the best and worst things that could ever happen?

Table 3(3) Aide-memoire for interviewing a child

(a) Description of child	– appearance, size, manner, dress, behaviour, activity.
(b) Parent-child interaction	– quality, separation.
(c) Mood	– sad, happy, anxious, calm, tears, laughter.
(d) Talk and thought	– spontaneity, logic, content.
(e) Rapport	– relationship to, and effect on, interviewer.
(f) Intelligence and development	– estimate of intelligence, age-appropriateness of development.
(g) Play	– involvement, quality, content, drawings.
(h) Fantasies	– three magic wishes, dreams, grow-up.

SPECIAL INVESTIGATIONS

Psychological tests are used to obtain additional information about the child, but there is considerable controversy regarding the validity and reliability of such tests. They are administered by psychologists who are trained in their interpretation and application. We will discuss only those tests that are in common use.

Intelligence tests

There is much dispute about the meaning of intelligence, and what intelligence tests measure. Intelligence is generally considered to involve the abilities to learn and reason. There is no generally accepted definition of intelligence. A useful definition is – the general all-round ability to perform mental tasks; an equally sound but rather cynical definition states – intelligence is what intelligence tests measure.

Intelligence is influenced by both genetic and environmental factors. It is usually quantified as the intelligence quotient (IQ) i.e. the index of a person's relative level of brightness as compared with others of his age. It is computed by using this formula:

$$IQ = {}^{MA}/_{CA} \times 100 \quad (MA = \text{Mental age, CA} = \text{Chronological age.})$$

One individual's IQ may vary with age for various reasons. The vagaries of IQ tests are such that different areas of intelligence are measured by different tests. Environmental influences may affect the score by 20 per cent or more. Development of intelligence is particularly rapid in the first four years of life, but relatively stable by the age of 17. The average IQ range is 70–130.

The most commonly used tests in the United Kingdom are:

(a) Wechsler Intelligence Scale for Children, Revised (WISC-R). The WISC-R is designed for use with children aged 6–16, and has separate verbal and performance sections.

(b) Wechsler Pre-school and Primary Scale of Intelligence (WPPSI). This test is a version of the WISC-R modified for testing 4–6 year-olds.

(c) Stanford-Binet. This is an American test based on a series of sub-tests divided for age range. It tends to be verbal rather than non-verbal, and is a useful indicator of educational potential. It is applicable to any age-group from 2 to adulthood.

(d) Raven's Matrices. This is a British test, entirely non-verbal, suitable for children aged 5–11, which should be combined with a verbal test. Its advantage is that its use does not depend upon the spoken word, so that it may be applied to children who are deaf or dumb or unable to speak (aphasic) or non-English-speaking.

(e) Merrill-Palmer Scale. This test is used for children aged 1½–6, and gives a general estimate of a child's abilities.

Specific developmental tests

Such tests differ from intelligence tests in measuring specific aspects

Table 3(4) Developmental milestones (There is considerable variation between children for all these milestones)

approximate age of commencement	motor	vision and manipulation	hearing and speech	social behaviour
6 weeks	Holds head up momentarily			Smiles
3 months	Lifts head up	Watches movement Holds rattle	Vocalizes Listens	Shows pleasure
6 months	Rolls over Sits	Reaches for toys Objects to mouth Feeds from cup	Babbles	Enjoys toys Alert, interested
9 months	Crawls Stands holding-on	Looks for dropped toy	Begins to localize sound	Separation anxiety Coy with strangers Plays 'peep-bo'
1 year	Stands unsupported Walking soon	Deliberately drops objects and watches them	Understands commands First words	Symbolic and investigative play; waves 'bye-bye'; co-operates with dressing
1½ years	Rapid increase in motor skills Picks up toy from floor without falling	Builds towers with 3 bricks Scribbles	Several words	Starts using potty Plays alongside other children
2 years	Runs, climbs stairs Jumps	Tower of 6 bricks	Simple phrase	Dry and clean by day Co-operative play Loses separation anxiety
3 years	Can stand on one foot Ride tricycle	Tower of 9 bricks Can draw a circle	Sentences	Knows own sex Sexual curiosity No separation anxiety
4 years	Can hop	Crude drawings of multiple objects	Comprehensive speech	Dresses and undresses with assistance
5 years	Can skip, ride bicycle		Fluent speech	Dresses and washes without assistance

of development, whereas intelligence tests evaluate overall abilities. *Table 3(4)* outlines the key developmental milestones, though these are necessarily very approximate.

(a) Griffiths scale. The Griffiths is used for children aged 0–24 months, and measures development in five areas, locomotor, personal-social, hearing and speech, eye and hand co-ordination, and performance.

(b) Neale Reading Test. This is the most commonly used of the reading tests and is primarily designed to test accuracy. It consists of a series of graded prose passages but also has questions on comprehension. (Arithmetic and spelling tests are available but little used.)

(c) Reynell Developmental Language Scale. This test is useful in the assessment of children with delayed language development, and comprises two scales, one for measuring verbal comprehension, and the other verbal expression.

(d) Symbolic Play Tests. A young child's ability to use symbolic play is an important differentiating feature when it is uncertain whether a child is autistic, mentally handicapped, or suffering from specific language problems. There are a number of symbolic play tests.

The importance of both intelligence and developmental tests lies not simply in obtaining a score, but in the differences in results on the subtests, and the manner in which the child tackles the tests. The comments made by the psychologist are often of more importance than the actual scores.

'Projective' tests

These are of very doubtful validity as the interpretation of the way the test has been done depends very much on the psychologist's own theoretical viewpoint. They can, however, be a useful medium for discussion with a child of his fantasies. Well-known projective tests include the Draw-a-Person test (self-explicit) and the Rorschach in which the child is asked to guess what a variety of ink blots represent.

The Bene-Anthony test is used to find out a child's perception of himself in relation to this family. A series of cards with messages on them is 'posted' into figures, representing family members, for example 'This person loves me', 'I get cross with this person'.

Repertory Grids are a form of 'personal map' based on the theory of personal constructs originally described by Kelly (1955) but most clearly explained by Bannister and Fransella (1971).

Physical examination

Routine physical examination is of limited value in child psychiatry. It is indicated in children with mental retardation or developmental delay, children who are suspected of any neurological disorder, and any child who has behavioural or other problems over and above physical illness or handicap. Some psychiatrists insist on examining children who are overactive, enuretic, or encopretic. However, in most instances, it is usually fairly obvious from a carefully elicited history whether a physical disorder is likely to be present and responsible for the presenting problems.

Electro-encephalogram

This is a record of the variations in electrical activity between the different parts of the brain, and may provide evidence of cerebral pathology. Its use is limited in child psychiatry.

THE MANAGEMENT PLAN AND CHOICE OF INTERVENTION

As the final part of the initial assessment the worker should make a plan of the interventions he considers most appropriate. There is an almost endless list of interventions that could be made by the worker himself or by others, although the choice of intervention will inevitably be limited by the resources and policy of the agency, the availability of desired resources in the community, the acceptability of a particular intervention to the family members, and the training and experience of the worker making the assessment. In later chapters we discuss in some detail a number of different interventions but these are by no means exclusive and many interventions on different levels can be carried out simultaneously. Interventions may be also carried out on behalf of groups of clients, for example, setting up a club for the parents of overactive children, or organizing a safe play area for children living in high-rise flats. Changes in central government policy or broader local government policy are unmanageable aims on behalf of individual clients, but agencies do have a responsibility to press for relevant changes (see Chapter 10) and each individual social worker's experiences should contribute towards formulation of any action.

In Chapter 9 we discuss the necessity of developing skills in consultation and liaison as part of the overall management of a case.

The following example brings together some of the points made in the preceding section.

Sample individual formulation

Sarah is the 8 year-old eldest child of working-class parents in their mid-30s who have two other children aged 6 and 4. She has a one-year history of poor relationships both with her family and at school, tending to be surly, defiant, and withdrawn. She has suffered for five years from a moderate degree of asthma necessitating the use of daily medication, but has no other physical, intellectual, or developmental problems. Her behaviour alienates her from her peers, and irritates and upsets both her teachers and her parents. The asthma prevents her from participating in many school activities, and she has fallen behind in her work.

The family live in a council flat and have accumulated some debts since the father left them for a six-month period eighteen months previously. The marital relationship remains poor, and the father has refused to attend the clinic saying it is no one else's business. His wife is overburdened by three young children, financial worries, and lack of support. The two younger children are both very active and mischievous, and the 6 year-old still wets his bed adding to his mother's chores.

In the interview, Sarah remained sullen and withdrawn. She made no spontaneous comments and replied to questions monosyllabically. In play and drawings she showed considerable confusion and ambivalence about family relationships. Her mother was harassed, tired, guilt-laden, and despairing.

Sarah's behaviour seems to be a reaction to the marital disharmony and upheaval, although the asthma, and the consequent physical impairment, missed schooling, and academic underachievement are likely to have adversely affected her self-image. The resultant emotional stresses and the parents' inability to help her may have further aggravated the asthma.

In view of the lack of co-operation from Sarah's father, a family-based intervention is not feasible. Sarah requires help in understanding and expressing more acceptably her feelings of ambivalence towards her parents, and her fears of further separations. This may be achieved by a short series of meetings with either Sarah alone, or together with her mother. Sarah's mother would benefit from the opportunity to share her feelings and to discuss alternative ways of dealing with all the difficulties. This might best be achieved by her having some sessions for herself. Liaison with the various firms to which money is owed is indicated, in particular the electricity board, pointing out the difficulties the family have experienced, and the dangers for Sarah should electricity be cut off. Discussions with the school are also indicated, with a view to the provision of remedial help for Sarah. The general practitioner should be consulted with regard to the management of Sarah's asthma, and her brother's enuresis. If necessary, referral to an enuresis or child guidance clinic should be organized.

Conclusions

Whatever the interviewer's theoretical orientation, we consider an initial family assessment (including an assessment of the family in relation to the outside world) to be mandatory if a truly comprehensive view of the problem is to be obtained. Additional information should be acquired from other professionals involved, such as the general practitioner and teacher. A comprehensive assessment may require a number of meetings. Once this has been completed, a formulation should be prepared, and a plan of management outlined. A one-page statement of the formulation and management plan is of infinitely more value than ten or more pages of history and background. The preparation of such a formulation forces the interviewer to take a clear view of the problems, define the interventions to be used, the methods by which these may be achieved, and to have recognizable goals, which may be evaluated. As much of the formulation as seems appropriate should be shared with the family and future plans discussed with them. Specific types of intervention are outlined in succeeding chapters.

4

Common presenting problems

Introduction

The origins of childhood disturbance, the perpetuating factors, and the remedies must be considered in terms of interactions between the child, his family, and the outside world. Nonetheless, for many years, child psychiatrists have used child-orientated diagnostic categories and classification schemes when considering childhood disturbance. The potential advantages of this 'labelling' approach are that they may enhance reliable communication between clinicians and/or researchers, provide a framework within which concepts of distinct disorders may be refined, and allow for more careful planning and administration of appropriate services (Hill 1979: 101). The major disadvantage arises from the *tendency* to respond to the 'label' as opposed to the complex combination of events that have led to the current situation. We believe that the potential advantages might outweigh the disadvantages if that potential were fulfilled. As it is, communication is very unreliable; for example, the terms dyslexia, minimal brain dysfunction, hyperkinesis, and schizophrenia, have different meanings not only in Britain and North America but even within Britain. Further, the more attempts are made to define separate disorders, the clearer it becomes that there is considerable overlap. Finally, there is little evidence that the weighty attempts to produce a meaningful system of classification have led to improved services.

More recently, child psychiatrists have started using a multi-axial scheme for classification in which consideration is given to (1) the clinical psychiatric syndrome, (2) the intellectual level, (3) developmental delays, (4) associated physical conditions, and (5) associated psycho-social factors (Rutter, Shaffer, and Sturge 1975). Although the fifth axis is at this stage very inadequate, the scheme in general seems to be the most satisfactory available, in that it does make an attempt to broaden the perspective from the individual in isolation. Considerably more research is required before a truly comprehensive classification scheme becomes available.

Nonetheless, the reader is likely to encounter various diagnostic labels and specific problems in the course of his or her work, therefore we include in this chapter a description of the principal diagnostic categories, so that an understanding of them may be promoted. Under each category we briefly discuss management, and the reader is referred to the appropriate chapter for a fuller discussion of the specific approaches. Whatever the presenting problem, the primary focus for intervention should be the family, with any other specific techniques being incorporated in this context. From time to time we refer to certain self-help or support groups. Their full addresses can be found elsewhere (Russell 1976).

Diagnostic categories (1) – emotional disorders

These are inappropriate reactions to stress, occur in about 2½–5 per cent of the pre-adolescent population, and affect the sexes equally. Such disorders need to be differentiated from normal behaviour, and mild, transient, emotional disturbances which are part of growing-up. A 2 year-old who is wary of separating from his mother is behaving normally. A 5 year-old who has previously separated happily, but on starting school becomes clinging for a few weeks is showing a transient emotional disturbance. A 12 year-old who refuses to go to school, play with peers, or leave his mother, has an emotional disorder. The most important of these are:

(I) FEARS AND PHOBIAS

The emotional responses to external threats such as dogs, the dark, or burglars are known as 'fears'. Most children develop such fears at some stage. When fears become persistent, excessive, and out of all proportion to the situation, they are known as 'phobias'. Children's fears are influenced by personal experiences, their social skills and confidence, and the reactions of their parents and others. A child who is bitten by a dog is more likely to develop a dog phobia than one who is not, and especially if one or both parents are also fearful of dogs, or are unable to handle the situation in a calm and reassuring way. A child with poor social skills, and who lacks confidence, is also more prone to excessive fears, particularly relating to separation, school, and social situations.

Management

Fears and phobias are most successfully managed by using various behavioural methods within the context of the family approach.

(II) SCHOOL-REFUSAL (SCHOOL PHOBIA)

These terms are often used interchangeably, although 'school phobia' should really be confined to those instances when the cause of the anxiety is within the school. School-refusers are children who are persistently absent from school for long periods of time, and who instead remain at or near home with (usually) their mother. Whilst at home the child seems happy and well, but if threatened with or taken to school he becomes miserable and fearful. There is often no obvious precipitating factor, and usually there are no obvious causes for the problem at school.

This is a different picture from that of truancy in which the onset is more insidious, the child makes no fuss about going to school, the parents think he is at school, and often he will attend for part of the time. When not at school, the truant is often with friends, and may be involved in anti-social or delinquent activity. Hersov (1976: 457) has shown that there is also a complete contrast in family background and attitudes between truants and school-refusers. In diagnostic terms, the school-refuser has an emotional disorder, and the truant a conduct disorder.

The reasons for school-refusal are not totally clear. In some children, anxiety is mainly related to some aspect of the school situation, whilst in others the main anxiety is about leaving home, and separating from parents. Authorities differ on the relative significance and incidence of these considerations (Hersov 1976: 462). However, there is no doubt that parental anxiety in response to the child's anxiety can aggravate the situation. In some instances, the child is kept at home by the mother for such reasons as providing company to counteract loneliness, or because the mother is projecting her own fears onto the child.

A less well-recognized manifestation of school-refusal is the occurrence of a variety of physical symptoms for which can be found no organic cause, such as headache, fever, limb pains, or abdominal pains. When these occur on week-days but not week-ends, during the term but not the holidays, the reason becomes clear.

Management

Management of school-refusal requires attention to a wide variety of factors, in the school, at home, and in the child himself. A detailed assessment must be made of the relative contributions of each of these to the problem. Firstly, what is the school's view of the problem, do they recognize any particular problems for the child, either with a teacher, a lesson or activity, or peers? Secondly, what difficulties are there at home that may precipitate or aggravate the problem? Is anyone ill, is there marital disharmony or violence, is anyone depressed, how do the parents react to the child's refusal to go to school? Finally, what is the child's view of the problem? Does he have any particular worries at school, what lessons or activities bother him, how does he get on with his peers, is he bullied?

By building up a detailed profile, we are able to prepare a formulation of the problem (see Chapter 3) and to plan management. Attention should be paid to anything at school that needs remedy. The child may require remedial help for a particular subject he is worried about, or a change of teacher if he is frightened of one particular person. It may be necessary to prevent bullying, and the child may require help to overcome shyness about undressing in front of friends. Temporary exemption from certain activities may be helpful in getting him back to school.

More specific forms of therapy may be needed for the child and/or his family. Some advocate an immediate and, if necessary, forced return to school, whilst others favour a gradual re-introduction of the child into school. Waldfogel, Coolidge, and Hahn (1957) advise an individual psychotherapeutic approach, and Skynner (1976) prefers a family approach. Hersov (1976) has reviewed the indications for the in-patient treatment of school-refusal. These include early onset and persistence over time, intense resistance of the child, physical battles with the child, increasing social isolation of the child, and failure of carefully planned out-patient treatment.

We agree with Hersov that school-refusal is a whole-family problem, and that even when there is obvious maternal pathology we want to know how the remainder of the family might precipitate, aggravate, and maintain this. Thus, we recommend a whole-family approach which allows also for behavioural modification methods of encouraging return to school, but we concentrate also on the meaning behind the symptom, the cause of the school-refusal. On the whole, we do not favour residential treatment as this seems to be taking the child away from the problem without necessarily tackling its cause at source. Adequate treatment of the underlying conditions apppears to be more important than returning the child to school when it comes to assessing long-term outlook (Baker and Wills 1979). Without such treatment there is a greater risk of adult psychiatric illness and particularly agoraphobia.

(III)   MISERY, UNHAPPINESS, AND DEPRESSION

Like worries and fears, misery and unhappiness are universally experienced feelings, and every normal child is subject to such states from time to time. It only becomes abnormal if these emotions are sufficiently severe or prolonged to interfere with the child's life.

'Depression' is a word that may be used in three different senses – to describe a mood, a syndrome (i.e. a number of symptoms), or an illness. To confound the issue, the syndrome and illness known in adult life as depression are very rare in childhood. It is therefore not surprising that the use of the term in childhood is clouded in confusion, and that there are many contradictory views expressed about childhood depression. We use the word depression to signify a state of intense sadness, associated with feelings of despair. There may also be eating, sleeping, and other disturbances.

Susan, 11, is a fairly typical example of a depressed child. She had a three-month history of loss of appetite, poor sleep, and inability to concentrate. She had become moody, and tearful, and would spend hours at a time lying on her bed moping. She seemed to have no interest in anything, and made no effort to contact her friends.

Others have used the expressions 'depressive equivalent' or 'masked depression' by which are meant emotional disorders which signify that the child is depressed but which present in a disguised way, such as with aggression or anti-social activity, hyperactivity, psychosomatic illness, learning problems, school refusal, or relationship difficulties. We doubt the usefulness of these concepts.

In adolescence, the concept of depression becomes only marginally less confusing. The normal adolescent has periods of moodiness and negativism, but the depressed adolescent may also manifest a far more persistent and severe mood disturbance, resembling depressive illnesses seen in adults. Thoughts of suicide are common, but attempted suicide is uncommon, whilst completed suicide is very rare (Shaffer 1974). There are now a number of reports of attempted suicide in young children (Fritz 1980).

There are many possible causes of depressive disorder in childhood, and in general terms these may be described as any acute or chronic stress whether in the family, at school, or in peer-relationships. The reaction to such stresses is dependent upon such factors as the child's personality, previous experiences, and parental handling.

Management

A broad approach is required. Obviously, remedial factors should receive attention, but usually individual or family therapy is necessary. Anti-depressant medication has very little value in childhood depression, despite determined but unsubstantiated claims to the contrary (Frommer 1972). It is indicated in adolescent depression when the presentation resembles the adult form, but additional modes of help are still required to alleviate the causes of the problem.

Outcome

Satisfactory outcome is dependent upon correct formulation and appropriate management. There is no evidence that depressed children become depressed adults, though if the problem remains untreated the child is clearly more at risk of emotional problems in adult life.

The subject has been comprehensively reviewed by Graham (1973).

(iv) OBSESSIONS

'Obsessional behaviour' in childhood is common and is usually expressed in such rituals as the avoidance of stepping on cracks between paving-stones or the insistence on a particular sequence of events at bed-times. Such phenomena may be considered as part of normal development and are usually self-limiting. 'Obsessional disorders' consist of the recurrent acting-out of irresistible urges to the extent that the child becomes handicapped by them. Such disorders are rare in childhood, and hardly ever seen below the age of 6. The onset is usually gradual with no obvious precipitating cause. There is often a family history of similar problems, and there is frequently an association with phobias. The families tend to have high standards, but there is no evidence that toilet-training is unduly rigid, punitive or prolonged, contrary to the assertion of some psychoanalytic theorists.

The cause of obsessional disorders is, perhaps predictably, hotly debated. There is, however, general agreement that both obsessional behaviour and disorders are a reaction to anxiety, a way of reducing anxiety (Carr, A. 1974). Analytical theory states that obsessional defences serve to keep the ego uncontaminated by instinctual forces (Rycroft 1968). Learning theorists state that such behaviour may be a learned avoidance-response to childhood conflict (Meyer and Chesser 1970). It has also been stated that obsessional disorders in children can frequently be seen as an attempt to control other members of the family (Leigh, Pare, and Marks 1972).

Bill, 9, was referred by his general practitioner because his parents were concerned about his need to touch everything he saw. He would spend ten minutes touching all the objects in any room he entered. He also felt a strong urge to hit himself. His mother has had life-long obsessional features, and made persistent and unrealistic demands for Bill to be perfectly behaved and immaculately dressed.

Management

Obsessional disorders are amongst the most difficult to treat. In adults, behaviour therapy seems to be more effective than psychotherapy or medication, but intractable cases may require all three. In children, there are very few studies from which we can decide how best to treat such problems. Behavioural approaches seem to hold most promise from our clinical experience, though the whole family requires considerable help and should be involved in the management. Follow-up studies indicate a rather poor outcome, with considerable residual handicap.

(v) HYSTERIA

The notion of hysteria derives from the ancient Greeks, who applied the term solely to diseases of women, explained as being due to malfunction of the uterus (*ustera*). It is therefore not surprising that the terms 'hysteria' and 'hysterical' are rarely used in their medically accepted sense, i.e. as a disorder characterized by the presence of physical symptoms, but no evidence of any disease, with behaviour suggesting that the symptoms fulfil a psychological function. The physical symptoms take the form of disorders of memory, consciousness, intellect, movement, or sensation. Thus, the 'patient' may complain of, for example, loss of memory or voice, paralysis, blindness, deafness, or appear drowsy and disorientated. The symptoms are often associated with an inappropriate lack of concern, known as *belle indifférence*.

'Hysterical' may be applied to (i) a symptom as above, e.g. hysterical blindness, (ii) a personality, implying a predisposition to hysterical symptoms, or (iii) behaviour, implying a histrionic quality.

Most of the information on hysterical disorders in childhood is to be found in a study by Caplan (1970). Such disorders are rare, probably less than 1 per cent of clinic referrals, and usually present as loss of sight or voice, abnormal gait or paralysis, fits or faints, and severe pain. They occur equally between the sexes before puberty, but females far exceed males after puberty. Precipitating factors are hard to elicit, though occasionally a relative has recently had an illness affecting the same part of the body. Occasionally 'hysterical illness' later transpires to be true organic illness (Rivinus, Jannison, and Graham 1975).

Management

This usually invoves hospital admission, if only to exclude organic disease. Behaviour therapy, psychotherapy, or family therapy may all be beneficial, though it is very important that there is careful liaison between the paediatrician and whoever else is involved (Dubowitz and Hersov 1976). Most children eventually recover fully.

(VI) ELECTIVE MUTISM

This condition occurs only in children. Despite normal language development, the child is mute in certain situations, but not others. Usually such children speak at home with the family, but not in the presence of strangers, nor at school. They are often also shy, timid, and anxious. Onset is around the time of starting school, and it occurs equally between the sexes. Treatment is usually ultimately successful, whether it be psychotherapy, behaviour therapy, or family therapy, though it may sometimes need to be continued over a long period.

(VII) SHYNESS

Shyness is a natural phenomenon in certain stages of childhood. A baby first shows shyness between 6–12 months of age. This persists in varying degrees during the pre-school years, gradually diminishes in intensity, but may recur in adolescence. It is only abnormal if it does not occur at all, or if it is so severe that it interferes with the child's ability to be involved in age-appropriate behaviour. Thus, most pre-school children show initial shyness in the presence of strangers, but soon overcome it.

Shyness may be accompanied by sensitivity and social withdrawal or isolation. It is partly a temperamental characteristic but may be aggravated by the environment and experience. The child who never mixes with strangers is unlikely to overcome his natural shyness, and the child who is coerced, mocked, or punished for it will withdraw further. Some children with elective mutism are excessively shy.

Management

Management of shyness involves eliciting any obvious causes, discouraging negative reactions, building up self-esteem and pride, and gently encouraging gradual contact, first alongside other children and then involvement in play or activities with them. Parents and teachers need to be sympathetic, understanding, and patient.

Diagnostic categories (2) – anti-social behaviour disorders

Introduction

The concept of these disorders is social rather than medical. Such children are not fitting into socially-accepted norms of behaviour and fail to correct their deviation in response to social sanctions (Wardle 1974). Alternatively, they may be reacting to the absence of such sanctions, or more influenced by their peer-group whose own behaviour is anti-social. Their behaviour is predominantly negativistic, aggressive, destructive, defiant, and disobedient. Lying, bullying, truancy, and stealing may occur.

Some such children manifest this behaviour in isolation from others, and may be unable to make peer-relationships. Others acquire the values of behaviour of a delinquent peer group to whom they are loyal, and with whom they join in expressing their anti-social behaviour. Occasionally, the disorder is compulsive in origin, for example, stealing. Many children who fit into this category also have signs of emotional disorders.

Many authorities (for example, Hill 1979: 117) make a distinction between two major forms of anti-social behaviour – delinquency and conduct disorders; delinquency is defined as 'law-breaking behaviour, no more', whereas children with conduct disorders show 'excessive behaviour as judged by age-related norms, but the child is also either suffering or his personal development is being seriously impeded'. Such a distinction is dubious. Law-breakers are only so defined because they are caught and convicted. Whether or not an anti-social child is convicted may depend on a wide variety of variables such as his age, appearance, race, class, intelligence, luck, ability to obtain good legal support and advice, and the varying methods used to deal with such children, other than bringing them to court.

(I) INCIDENCE

The prevalence figures for anti-social behaviour in children vary depending upon the definition used and, as Rutter, Shaffer, and Sturge (1975) have shown, whether the population studied is urban or rural. Generally, the incidence is about twice as high in urban settings. In one London study it was shown that as many as 25 per cent of adolescent boys are convicted at some time (West and Farrington 1973). Berger, Yule, and Rutter (1975) suggest that this geographical difference is due to a combination of stresses, associated with inner city life, and mediated through the family. This phenomenon also seems to relate to a wide variety of other childhood psychiatric problems.

(II) AETIOLOGY

Factors commonly found to be antecedents of anti-social behaviour may be most readily considered under the same three headings as used in the chapter on assessment – the family, the environment, and the individual.

The family

Doane (1978) in her review of family interaction research noted that families of delinquents tend to be rather rigidly structured, i.e. the hierarchy is very clearly-defined and there is no room for change or adaptation. Parental discord, violence, and criminality have all been recognized as important predisposing factors (for example, West and Farrington 1973). The parental behaviour acts as a model for the child, whilst the low levels of stability, security, and consistency reduce the child's chances of developing a secure and loving relationship with its parents, and so increase the likelihood of various disorders (Rutter 1972). Parental loss and broken homes also increase the likelihood of such problems for similar reasons. Large family size and overcrowding have been reported to correlate with delinquency, but as they also correlate with so many other factors predisposing to delinquency, it is not clear whether the relationship is causal (Rutter, Tizard, and Whitmore 1970).

Social factors

Newson and Newson (1976) have shown that even by the age of 7, children from lower social classes tend to be more aggressive and destructive than middle-class children. In the past, such findings have been attributed to more coercive child-rearing practices of lower-class mothers, with a more aggressive and less nurturing approach (for example, Minton, Kagan, and Levine 1971), but Rutter, Tizard, and Whitmore (1970) suggest that social class is associated with conduct disorder (and other problems) because of such factors as low IQ and learning difficulties. Further, Rutter and Madge (1976) suggest that social problems such as poverty pre-dispose to delinquency not directly, but because of consequent family difficulties.

The significance of the neighbourhood and the school as causative factors has also been documented. Certain 'delinquent areas' can be identified where anti-social behaviour is not only well established but persists over a period of several years (Power, Benn, and Morris 1972). Similarly, some schools seem to have a far higher incidence of anti-social behaviour than others, with these differences being maintained over time, even though their pupils may come from the same area. It is suggested that such differences may be due to the respective cultures of the school (Rutter *et al.* 1979). Schools that had a positive effect on the children emphasized academic achievement, provided good conditions for the pupils, used incentives and rewards rather than punishments, provided responsibility for the children and encouraged a high degree of teacher involvement in the lessons. Schools lacking such features were more likely to have an adverse effect on the children.

Individual factors

There is a striking sex difference in the incidence of anti-social behaviour with boys being far more at risk than girls, whatever the age. Early experience of deprivation is a major pre-disposing factor in both sexes (Wolkind and Rutter 1973) although for boys the trigger seems to be the lack of contact with father, whereas for girls prolonged early experiences of residential care seems more important (Wolkind 1974b). Temperamental characteristics render some children more difficult to raise (Graham, Rutter, and George 1973) whilst brain damage, and the effects of medication for associated epilepsy, may also contribute to such problems. There is also a strong and possibly causal association between learning (particularly reading) difficulties and anti-social behaviour (Rutter, Tizard, and Whitmore 1970).

A fuller discussion of the causes of childhood disorders is to be found in Chapter 2. The complexities of aetiology with the likelihood of a number of factors interacting is typified by anti-social behaviour problems.

(III) MANAGEMENT

A very careful and comprehensive assessment of the relative contribution of family, social, and individual factors is essential, before a rational programme of interventions can be constructed. Consider, for example, a child with learning difficulties who attends a school whose attitude tends to be punitive and which has no remedial facilities; further, the family is large and lives in overcrowded and poor quality housing, and family life is characterized by inconsistency and discord, with no ability to change. Such a child is likely to benefit only slightly from help aimed at just one of these factors. Certainly the child requires assistance for his learning difficulties, and the school might well value advice on management in the classroom. The possibility of improved housing circumstances should be investigated, and attempts made to help the family overcome some, at least, of its relationship difficulties. It is very unlikely that only the one child is suffering from such adverse circumstances.

There is no satisfactory evidence to show casework or psychotherapy, however intensive, is of value for such children or their families. However, behavioural modification techniques (see Chapter 8) do seem to improve the outlook, especially when there is involvement of the teacher (Becker *et al.* 1967), the parents (Johnson and Katz 1973), and the whole family (Alexander and Parsons 1973). The outcome for such children is far from promising. Both short (Graham and Rutter 1973) and long-term (Robins 1966) studies indicate a high rate of disturbance at follow-up. There is a strong association between anti-social behaviour in children or adolescents and adult sociopathy, such as disregard for social obligations, lack of feelings for others, abnormal aggression, and irresponsibility. It is hoped that future studies of carefully co-ordinated and fully comprehensive treatment approaches will produce more encouraging results.

Diagnostic categories (3) – childhood psychoses

Introduction

A psychosis is a disorder involving such impairment of mental function that there is conspicuously disturbed behaviour, a lack of insight, and adequate contact with reality, and an inability to meet some ordinary demands of life. Although mentally retarded children can suffer from psychotic disorders, mental retardation itself is not considered to be a psychosis.

In childhood, psychotic disorders are rare, and the majority of readers may only meet them once or twice in a professional lifetime. Such disorders as do occur are all very different, and their inclusion together under the one heading is a matter of convenience. Autism is the most important disorder in this category.

(i) AUTISM (also known as infantile autism, childhood autism,
infantile psychosis, Kanner's Syndrome)

Autistic children have the following features:
(a) onset before age of 2½; (b) severe difficulties in socialization; (c) severe delay and difficulties in understanding and using language; (d) obsessional insistence on sameness; (e) gaze-avoidance, and (f) lack of symbolic play.
Some but not all autistic children will also show evidence of one or more of the following:
(g) repetitive and ritualistic movements; (h) short attention-span, and (i) self-injury.

Many autistic children are clearly abnormal from a very early age but some only manifest their difficulties in the second or third year of life. The incidence is about 1/2500, the sex-ratio equal, and, for reasons which are not yet clear, there is a predominance from social classes I and II. Autism appears to be due to an inborn specific cognitive deficit involving the inability to acquire an inner language (Rutter 1974). Environmental factors are not of primary significance. Autistic children vary in overall intelligence, though the majority have an IQ below 70. It should be noted that many mentally retarded children have some autistic features, but this does not mean that they are autistic.

Management

This is focused on aiding social and linguistic development, avoiding secondary handicaps, and supporting the family. It should be started as early as possible. The parents require considerable guidance on management, as well as the usual forms of support. Special schooling should be provided as early as possible.

The role of the social worker in the overall management of autism is outlined by Rutter and Sussenwein (1971). The effective linking of casework and behavioural modification techniques is described by Howlin *et al.* (1973) and the place of the school by Rutter and Bartak (1973).

Outcome

Sixty per cent of autistic children remain severely handicapped and totally unable to lead an independent life, 15 per cent make a fair social adjustment, and the remaining 25 per cent are intermediate. Good predictive factors include an IQ above 70, the acquisition of useful speech by the age of 5, and harmonious, middle-class backgrounds (Rutter 1974).

(II)   OTHER PSYCHOSES IN CHILDHOOD

Schizophrenia and manic-depressive illness are both very rare before puberty, and although they do occur in adolescence, the incidence is much lower than in adult life. They are both similar conditions to those affecting adults, and the interested reader is referred to a useful description by Steinberg (1976: 748–70). It is also worth reading the original account of the double-bind hypothesis (Bateson *et al.* 1956) which seeks to explain the onset of schizophrenia as a response to an intolerable relationship between the 'patient' and (usually) his mother. This was the first attempt to understand mental illness from an interactional view, as opposed to the perspective of individual psychopathology.

Diagnostic categories (4) – specific problems

There are a number of problems that do not fit into any specific diagnostic category, but which warrant detailed consideration because of their frequency or complexity.

(I) SLEEP PROBLEMS

Social workers frequently have clients who complain bitterly about their child's sleep disturbances. As Illingworth (1979: 246) states: 'Most children sooner or later in their first four years develop sleep problems.' The corollary to this is that most parents will also have sleep problems, leading to tiredness, irritability, impaired functioning, despair, and resentment. Such conditions are hardly conducive to good parental care, especially if the sleep disturbance continues for several months. It is perfectly possible to offer practical help in such circumstances, providing the social worker is aware of the fundamental issues. It is important to recognize that children have different sleep requirements and patterns, and that if a child is not tired and irritable he is getting enough sleep. There is no evidence to show that frequent waking is due to parental mismanagement (Bernal 1973, Blurton-Jones *et al.* 1978).

Bedtime rituals are also common. They can vary from such simple patterns as requiring a particular parent to read a particular story, to highly complex sequences lasting up to half an hour or more. The purpose is in part comforting, and in part the postponing of the moment of departure of the parent. Providing the parents handle the situation sensibly, being neither too intolerant nor too compliant, such rituals usually disappear quite quickly.

Sleeptalking and *sleepwalking* are often causes of concern to parents. The former is quite common and is only of significance if accompanied by obvious distress. Sleepwalking is more disturbing to parents. The child may appear to be awake and his walking may seem purposeful. It is usually difficult to wake the child. The cause is not clear, and the only necessary treatment is to ensure the child's safety.

Nightmares affect all children at some stage. Occasional episodes are perfectly normal and may be associated with unexpressed or unresolved fears and anxieties. Only if they are occurring very frequently need they be a cause for concern. Should this be happening, almost certainly there will be other indications of emotional problems.

Night-terrors are a very specific form of nightmare in which the child will suddenly awake in a state of extreme distress, often screaming or shouting incoherently. In such states the child is not easily pacified, unlike with a nightmare, and is usually unaware of the parental presence. The distress may subside only after five or ten minutes. The cause of these episodes is not known, nor are they necessarily associated with other problems. A small dose of Valium (diazepam) taken at bedtime often eliminates the problem.

Management

There is no clear dividing-line between a normal sleep-pattern and a sleep problem. One determinant is the parental tolerance. Whenever a parent expresses concern about a child's sleep-pattern, bedtime or night-time behaviour, a careful history should be taken to help determine whether this is within normal limits and whether there are other problems. As each child differs in his sleep requirements, attention must be paid to whether the child is suffering from insufficient sleep, and whether there may be some fundamental reason for disturbed sleep such as discomfort, pain, or hunger.

Very often all that is needed is counselling of parents to help them distinguish between normal and abnormal sleep patterns. Parents may need support through what is probably a relatively short-lived problem. Small doses of hypnotics over short periods are often useful to induce a more acceptable sleep-pattern and used carefully are harmless and non-addictive. Taking a restless baby into bed, if acceptable to the parents, is not harmful and indeed can be a helpful way of coping, providing the parents ensure that this is done only on a temporary basis.

The application of behavioural techniques has been shown to be useful for toddlers and older children with sleep disturbances.

(II) EATING AND FEEDING PROBLEMS

These are important because they are common and, when severe, a danger to the child's health. Further, they may be a source of great anxiety to the parents, for a child who does not feed is striking at the parents' basic confidence in their ability to care for the child. Feeding difficulties may be considered under five categories:

(a) *Food fads.* These are almost universal to some degree and rarely indicate serious problems. Generally, they arise from food-forcing or parental over-anxiety. They may vary from the dislike of one or two specific foods, possibly as a result of that food being linked with the memory of an unpleasant experience, to extreme faddishness in which the child may eat only one or two specific foods. This latter state usually arises as a result of extreme anxiety on the parents' part.

(b) *Food-refusal.* All children from time to time refuse their meals or dawdle over them, starting in the first year of life. The child may not be hungry, he may not like the taste, he may be angry or unhappy. Parental attempts to make children eat are readily defeated by blank refusal, further dawdling or vomiting. And so the scene is set for a lengthy battle which might be re-enacted every mealtime often for months or years. The parents may use a vast range of techniques in an attempt to win, including bribing, begging, blackmailing, and beating. But the child always wins.

This form of food-refusal should be distinguished from anorexia nervosa (pp. 83–5) which only very rarely affects pre-pubertal children, and has its own distinctive features.

Management

Management consists of carefully assessing the parental attitude to feeding, and providing basic guidelines for the parents. They need to be taught that it is never necessary to persuade or force a child to eat –

children have appetites sufficient for their needs, and their likes and dislikes should be respected. No special efforts need be made to encourage a child to eat. Parents are encouraged to conceal their anxiety by, for example, avoiding looking at the child's plate or making comments about how well or badly he is doing. He should sit at the table, or high-chair, and eat his food or leave it. If after a reasonable time, he is clearly not going to finish his meal, the food should be withdrawn without comment and the child encouraged to continue normal activities until the next mealtime. Sweets, cakes and suchlike should be avoided between meals if the child is eating insufficiently. When parents manage to maintain a consistent and unemotional approach, the problem disappears in the majority of cases.

Occasionally, food-refusal in pre-school children is associated with other problems such as sleep-disturbance, screaming episodes, behaviour problems, and failure-to-thrive. Such powerful combinations are usually an indicator of a more serious disturbance in the parent-child relationship. In these circumstances a far more comprehensive assessment of the family is required, and management may involve the provision of more intensive help such as family therapy, a pre-school day-centre (Bentovim 1973) or, in the most severe cases, admission of parent and child to a paediatric ward (Bingley *et al.* 1980).

(c) Overeating and obesity.   These are difficult terms to define. There is a value judgment in the former and a pejorative quality in the latter. Paediatricians describe a child as obese if the thickness of the skinfold at the back of the upper arm is greater than that of 90 per cent of children of the same age.

The causes of obesity are complex. At a simple level, it is clear that a child becomes obese because he overeats or is overfed. But not all children who eat more than their natural calorie requirements become overweight. It appears that there is a genetic factor which determines whether the additional calories are burned off or stored in the form of fat cells.

The psychological aspects of obesity are not clearly understood. Some children have learned from an early age that eating has a comforting component, so that whenever in distress they eat. As they become overweight, and suffer the emotional sequelae, so they need to eat more. Other children become overweight as a result of over-feeding by mothers who put undue emphasis on the value of food. Many grossly overweight children seem to have a particularly close relationship with their mothers. Some overweight children come from families in which most or all of the members are also overweight.

The sequelae of being overweight are numerous. There are a variety of physical consequences, the most serious of which are high blood pressure and heart disease. The psychological sequelae include peer-group rejection, isolation, and poor self-esteem. Obese children tend to be more stigmatized than children with any other handicap.

Mildly overweight children may be successfully treated by offering simple dietary advice to the child and parents, with instructions to ensure sufficient exercise. The more severely overweight children tend to be resistant to most interventions, and their motivation to lose weight is suspect. The parents, too, are frequently unco-operative. There is no evidence to show that any of the conventional methods of treatment are of value in these cases of intractable obesity. It may be helpful to consider such problems to be of the same order as drug or alcohol addiction. All the problems of an addiction will have to be tackled including the physical and psychological dependence, the apparent determination of the addict to kick the habit, but with early relapse, and anger towards the therapist for 'putting me through such agony'. Time may show that the most appropriate approach to childhood obesity is a combination of behaviour modification of the faulty eating patterns, and treatment of the family problems that have initiated and maintained the overeating.

There is no place for medication in the treatment of obesity, but children whose health, or indeed life are endangered may require hospital admission to help them achieve a safer weight.

(d) Pica. This is the ingestion of non-edible substances and is associated with severe emotional disturbance or deprivation, and with mental retardation. It is usually accompanied by other be-havioural problems. One of the dangers of pica is lead poisoning which can cause brain damage. Management of the condition involves treatment of the aggravating factors such as emotional deprivation or family turmoil. Behaviour modification techniques may be successfully employed for pica in mentally handicapped children.

(e) Polydypsia. This is excessive drinking, usually of water. In the absence of an organic cause such as diabetes, it should be considered to be a manifestation of a severe emotional disturbance, which requires a comprehensive assessment. The parents of such children often find it difficult to accept that there is no organic cause, and a careful liaison with the appropriate doctor may be necessary to overcome this resistance.

(III)   NOCTURNAL ENURESIS OR BED WETTING

This is the involuntary passage of urine during sleep, in the absence of a physical abnormality. It is a very common problem in childhood. Daytime voluntary control of the bladder does not occur until the age of 18 months at the earliest, and often very much later, whilst night-time control is rarely achieved before the age of 2. Many children do not gain total control until the age of 4 or 5. Indeed, about 10 per cent of children aged 5, 5 per cent of children aged 10, and 1 per cent in their teens, still wet their bed at least occasionally.

The reasons for this common problem are not at all clear. Several factors may contribute:

(a) There is a tendency for enuresis to run in families, suggesting a genetic component.

(b) There may sometimes be a delay in development of the neurological pathways which determine bladder control.

(c) Very occasionally, enuresis is associated with physical abnormalities in the urinary tract, or a disorder in the bladder's filling and emptying mechanism.

(d) Stresses may occur at the time when bladder control is usually achieved and thus interfere with its normal acquisition.

(e) Toilet-training may be unduly harsh and punitive or unusually lax, either of which can interfere with the development of bladder control.

(f) There may already exist an emotional disturbance which blocks the acquisition of bladder control.

(g) Environmental stresses may occur which cause a child who has gained control to regress and become enuretic.

The high incidence of enuresis in children's homes may be explained by the interaction of a number of these factors.

Management

The specific physiological mechanisms associated with bladder control and emptying are complex and not completely understood, which makes it difficult for there to be any certainty of the best means of treatment. Many techniques are available but none of them guarantees success. Help is required for any emotional or physical disturbance, and obvious stress factors should be alleviated where possible. Parents may require considerable assistance in adjusting their attitudes. One of the most useful techniques is the 'bell and pad alarm system' (see p. 143) whilst drugs such as Tofranil or Tryptizol (see p. 174) are useful in the short-term. General measures include fluid restriction for a couple of hours before bedtime, waking the child at about 10 p.m. or 11 p.m., and if necessary during the night, to empty his bladder, and star charts to reward the child for dry nights. Bladder training during the day may help. The child is encouraged to reduce the number of times he empties his bladder during the day, the rationale being that this might increase bladder capacity.

Diurnal (daytime) enuresis is a much less common problem and is often associated with a physical abnormality in the urinary tract. When this is not the case, there is usually a more general emotional disturbance requiring a comprehensive assessment and treatment. Star charts and rewards are probably the simplest and most effective specific treatment, but the underlying emotional problems will require considerable attention.

Both conditions tend to resolve spontaneously over time, and this is an important fact for both child and parents to know.

(iv) ENCOPRESIS

Encopresis – or faecal soiling – is a much less common disorder than enuresis, but it is more often an expression of serious emotional disturbance. About 1.5 per cent of children aged 7–8 are encopretic. Boys are affected three to four times more often than girls. There is considerable variation in the age at which bowel control is achieved but most children are clean by the age of 3.

There are three main categories of encopresis in children who are old enough to have bowel control, but with some overlap between the groups.

(a) Primary encopresis.   Some children do not gain bowel control and are often also enuretic. Such children may be unaware that they are soiling or unable to control their bowels. They tend to come from socially disadvantaged homes, they are often behind at school, have associated emotional problems, and parents who are themselves limited in intellect and personality. The faeces are of normal consistency and are always passed into the child's pants.

(b) Secondary encopresis.   This second group have acquired normal bowel control, but as part of a wider emotional disturbance have regressed and started soiling. Such children deposit their faeces in inappropriate places which, besides their pants, include cupboards, the corners of a room, or under a bed. Occasionally, such children may smear their faeces on walls, furniture, etc.

(c) Constipation with overflow.   The third group pass fluid faeces, over which they have no control. They are children who have become constipated either by deliberate withholding or by a more complex and possibly unconscious process. The deliberate withholding may be due to a fear of using the toilet or pot, or the result of a battle between child and parent, in which the parent pressurizes the child to use the pot, and the latter refuses. The parent responds in a punitive manner, and a vicious cycle is initiated. This pattern has been called 'the battle of the bowel'. The end result is severe constipation with partial blockage and consequent leakage of fluid motions, which understandably aggravates the already inflamed situation. Occasional withholding starts soon after the child commences a school at which the toilets are unsatisfactory. However, it is unlikely that this would be the only relevant factor for otherwise all the pupils at the school would become constipated!

Management

Management of encopresis is dependent upon the particular type of soiling. Treatment of the primary encopretic in which bowel control has not been previously attained is by the straightforward use of bowel training, perhaps incorporating a reward scheme for success. Associated emotional and social problems also require considerable attention. Secondary encopretic children who have already gained bowel control need a comprehensive assessment of their emotional environment. Almost inevitably there are family problems which will require alleviation, most effectively achieved by family therapy. Children who have constipation with overflow incontinence, and their families, should also be thoroughly assessed. The cause of the constipation must be determined, whether it be a pot or toilet-phobia or the result of a parent-child battle. (A third but infrequent cause is the presence of an anal fissure, or tear, which causes pain on defecation.) A carefully taken history will almost certainly elicit the cause. Management consists of specific treatment, such as laxatives, for the constipation. A toilet-phobia may be relieved by desensitization and rewards. Over-zealous parents need help to modify their attitudes and to learn to encourage and praise the child rather than pressurize and punish him.

Encopresis is a worrying and upsetting problem which can be rapidly alleviated by careful assessment and management.

(v) HYPERKINETIC SYNDROME

This is a rare disorder. The exact incidence is unclear because of the frequency with which it is wrongly diagnosed, but in the Isle of Wight Epidemiological Study, the incidence was 0.1 per cent. Boys are affected four times more frequently than girls. It is a most striking disorder, characterized by *extreme* overactivity in young children and associated features of very poor concentration, marked distractibility, and short attention-span. Parents and teachers describe such children as 'always on the go'. Such a description, however, is applied to many normal children who then become labelled as hyperkinetic or hyperactive, and consequently mismanaged. A majority of young children are very active, and there is nothing abnormal about this. What characterizes the hyperkinetic syndrome is the *inability* to stop moving, the inability to concentrate on anything (including television) for more than a minute or two, and the distractibility. It is as if such a child is driven by a powerful motor, with no brakes, and a steering system that has gone haywire!

Inevitably, these children have associated learning, behavioural, and emotional problems, and many suffer quite severe mood swings, alternating from elation to tears and back again, within a few moments. Occasionally, such children are of below-average intelligence and suffer delayed development of speech and other functions. Often, there is an underlying brain dysfunction (see pp. 78–9), but sometimes no obvious cause can be found. It has been fashionable recently in North America to explain hyperkinesis as an allergy to food additives. However, there is no evidence to confirm this, nor that complicated diets in any way improve the situation. It should also be noted that different diagnostic criteria are in use in North America.

It is generally reported that hyperkinetic children become *under-active* in adolescence. Unfortunately, by this time, they have usually suffered such emotional damage and they are so behind in education that they are severely socially handicapped.

Management

Treatment is not always very effective. The parents require emotional support and guidance on behavioural control. The child needs special educational help, and medication. Major tranquillizers such as Largactil and haloperidol may be of value, and para-doxically, drugs that act as stimulants in adults, such as ampheta-mines or Ritalin, sometimes reduce activity in hyperkinetic children. The trauma for the parents cannot be overestimated.

(VI) MINIMAL BRAIN DYSFUNCTION (MBD)

This is a term that is commonly used, especially in North America, and which is often associated with the hyperkinetic syndrome. Children who present with any of the following features may be 'labelled' as having MBD: (a) hyperactivity, (b) problems of co-ordination, movement, or perception, (c) disorders of attention, memory, or thinking, (e) speech and hearing difficulties, (f) im-pulsiveness, and (g) special investigations such as electroencephalo-gram or neurological examination in which the findings are equivocal.

The implication of MBD is that the child is suffering from a *limited* degree of brain dysfunction, in contrast to the child with obvious brain *damage* in whom there is clear evidence of such damage, with severe effects on the child's physical, emotional, and intellectual development.

In fact, there is no evidence for the existence of such a specific entity as MBD and it seems to be a term of convenience rather than having any specific value in the understanding of cause, treatment, and outlook. However, its use is officially sanctioned in North America to describe children of near-average, average, or above-average general intelligence with certain learning or behavioural disabilities ranging from mild to severe, which are associated with deviations of function of the central nervous system. Certainly, in this country, the term is also widely used, though not officially recognized, and the reader is likely to meet children who have been so labelled. Schmitt (1975) and many others have argued against the concept.

In our view, there is no harm in using such a term, so long as each child is assessed as an individual on his own merits. Due attention should be paid to the possible causes, and help offered for associated behaviour, learning, emotional, and physical problems. The parents and school also require support and advice.

(vii) tics

Tics are rapid, involuntary movements which recur frequently, and serve no purpose. Any part of the body may be involved, but most commonly they occur as blinking, wrinkling of the forehead, head movements, or shoulder-shrugging. Up to 10 per cent of all children may have tics at some time, most commonly between the ages of 5–10. They are much less common outside that age-range and occur more frequently in boys.

The cause is unknown, and predictably, emotional and physical factors have been incriminated, without any evidence. Tics are often associated with other features of emotional disturbance, but not aggression or depression. This suggests that possibly tics may be an alternative way of expressing emotions. This view is supported by the fact that tics disappear during sleep, and are increased by anxiety.

Parental concern, as is so often the case, may aggravate the problem by drawing attention to the tics, and increasing the child's concern and tension. Determined and punitive efforts to stop them have a similar adverse effect.

Most tics disappear spontaneously when ignored, but sometimes they may persist for long periods, and even into adult life. Simple explanation and reassurance is often sufficient treatment for uncomplicated problems. However, when there are additional features of emotional disturbance, more extensive assessment and therapy may be necessary. The usual claims have been made for the efficacy of psychotherapy, a variety of behavioural techniques, and various drugs. As yet, there is no definite evidence to suggest that one treatment is superior to another, but haloperidol does seem to be particularly useful in reducing the severity and frequency of tics.

Gilles de la Tourette's syndrome. This medical curiosity is extremely rare, but attracts attention because of its dramatic features. Such children experience body tics, and vocal tics (grunts) which later take the form of obscene utterances. The social effect is understandably devastating. Obviously, the outcome is much worse than for simple tics, and these children may become socially incapacitated. The full range of available treatments may be required.

(VIII) STAMMERING (OR STUTTERING)

Stammering involves an interruption in the normal rhythm of speech, because of an involuntary repetition, prolongation, or cessation of sound. Stammering affects approximately 1–2 per cent of school-children, and boys more than twice as often as girls. More than half of sufferers begin to stammer before the age of 5. There is usually no evidence of associated psychiatric disorder. There seems to be a strong genetic component in the causation, but anxiety and inappropriate handling may aggravate the problem.

It has been claimed that stammerers tend to come from homes in which there is excessive domination and discipline, over-protection and perfectionism, the mothers find life difficult, and the parents tend to be dissatisfied with their children and each other (Eisenson, 1971). A psychoanalytic explanation is quoted by Goodstein (1958: 189): 'stammering is a narcissistic neurosis and pre-genital conversion neurosis' (p. 189). A more helpful contribution to the understanding of stammering has been made by Johnson (1959) who states that children from 2½ years onwards become so excited in recounting what they have seen or heard that they stumble over themselves in a torrent of words, and stammering is then suspected by the mother. She seeks advice from well-meaning friends or relatives who confirm her suspicion, from which point parental anxiety reinforces the problem. Frenetic attempts to make the child speak properly only serve to make the child more self-conscious of his speech, and to exacerbate the difficulties.

About 50 per cent of stammerers improve naturally or without treatment. The milder the condition, the better the outlook. Treatment is aimed at reducing parental anxiety when the problem is mild or early, thus enabling them to help the child. In more severe instances, the assistance of a speech therapist will be required. Tranquillizers have also been recommended, but we reserve such treatment for only the most severe and intractable cases.

(IX) HABIT DISORDERS

Many children from time to time manifest one or more mannerisms or habits which may be either transient or long lasting. Among such habits are nail-biting, thumb-sucking, head-banging, breath-holding, and hair-pulling. Before we can determine the significance of the symptom, we must consider it in the context of the child and his environment. For example, a child who occasionally sucks his thumb but seems normal in every other respect need not be a cause for concern. However, a child who sucks his thumb, bites his nails, and bangs his head on the pillow at night, may well be giving vent to his feelings of anger and need for comfort. A child who so persistently pulls out hairs that he has bald patches, or holds his breath when thwarted until he faints, is clearly expressing a great deal of distress!

Children with habit disorders need to be fully assessed so that all possible environmental causes may be considered. Treatment should be aimed both at the cause of the problem and at helping the parents to manage the symptom appropriately. If a child finds he can only get attention from his parents when he bangs his head, he will continue to do so until they pay attention to his more positive aspects and they ignore the attention-seeking device. Some unusual movements may be due to rare medical conditions, and care should be taken to exclude these.

(X) PSYCHOSOMATIC PROBLEMS

A psychosomatic disorder is a physical condition in which emotional factors play an important part in causation or maintenance. Well-recognized childhood psychosomatic disorders include asthma, eczema, migraine, ulcerative colitis, obesity, peptic ulcer, some cases of failure-to-thrive, and periodic syndrome (one or more of recurrent abdominal pain, headaches, vomiting, fever, and limb pains). There is often disagreement about what constitutes a psychosomatic disorder, and the term is so widely misused that we feel it should be discarded.

We prefer to take a 'psychosomatic approach' to all illness. In other words, we should consider an illness from a biological, psychological, and social perspective. In even the most blatantly 'organic' conditions, such as cancer or kidney disease, psychological and social factors are of considerable significance.

We apply a four-tier model to all illness. We give due attention to; (1) the physical state of the child, (2) the child's psychological state, (3) the family, and (4) the environment (Lask 1981).

(1) Attention must be paid to the physical problem, whatever the diagnosis. The reality of the symptoms must be acknowledged – they are not imagined, made-up or manipulated, they are real. Without such an acknowledgement there is little chance of therapeutic progress. Physical methods of treatment may or may not be necessary, depending upon the diagnosis.

(2) Careful consideration must be given to the child's attitude to his illness, his degree of suggestibility, his ability to express openly his feelings and internal conflicts. The expression of emotion through physical symptoms – somatization – is a common psychological defence mechanism, in both children and adults.

(3) The family plays a significant part in any illness. The family's attitude to the illness, their methods of coping, and their feelings of guilt, sorrow, or resentment may all perpetuate the problem. The relationship between childhood illness and family dysfunction has been fully documented (Minuchin, Rosman, and Baker 1978).

(4) The extra-familial environment is also of great importance. Illness can be initiated or aggravated by poor school-attainment and adjustment and the attitude of peers, teachers, and the doctor.

The detailed assessment and management of psychosomatic disorders in children is discussed elsewhere (Lask 1981). In essence, each of the four tiers needs careful attention. We find that the most beneficial results are obtained by working with the whole family (see

Chapter 5) and liaising regularly with whichever other professionals are involved, including paediatricians, general practitioners, teachers, social workers, etc.

(XI) ANOREXIA NERVOSA

This condition is sometimes considered to be a psychosomatic disorder, but because of the reservations expressed above, and because of its complexity, we include it separately. Literally, the term means nervous loss of appetite. In reality, there is not so much a loss of appetite as a refusal to eat, or a fear of eating, accompanied by a marked loss of weight. Some sufferers have a healthy appetite, gorge themselves secretly, and then make themselves vomit. Frequently, such individuals are excessively active, and many have a distorted body image, i.e. they perceive themselves as being much fatter than they really are. The common feature in all cases is a fear of regaining normal weight. The 'anorectic' is preoccupied with food and calorie intake, and her whole life is devoted to losing weight. A variety of physiological changes occur in relation to the weight-loss, and in particular, menstruation ceases.

Traditionally, anorexia nervosa occurs in adolescent girls, and young women. Males account for only 10 per cent of cases, and very rarely does anorexia nervosa occur in pre-pubertal girls. It is a life-threatening condition and it has been reported that as many as 10 per cent of sufferers may die as a result of the condition (Warren 1968) although this is likely to be an overestimate.

The onset is often, but not always, related to a casual comment about the patient being slightly overweight. Many theories have been put forward to account for this serious problem. Some state that the 'anorectic' fears her developing sexuality and growing-up, and others that 'anorectics' have unusual internalized fantasies, such as eating being perceived as oral impregnation, and plumpness as pregnancy (Bruch 1973). Another view is that food-refusal may start initially for slimming purposes, but ultimately becomes an end in itself, reinforced by excessive parental attention and concern (Gore 1976). Linked to this view is the idea that the food-refusal plays an important part in family homeostasis with the symptom acting as a diversion from marital conflict (Minuchin, Rosman, and Baker 1978). Crisp (1977) states that the illness represents a psychobiological regression to childhood in the face of mounting conflict in adolescence.

It is difficult to make sense of some of these views, and certainly they represent diverse theoretical orientations. Even if we were to translate the 'language' used, we would not find they were all saying much the same thing, unlike, for example, in the analytical and learning theorists' explanations of phobias. We would have to be devotees of analytical theory to accept the oral impregnation view, and anyhow, such fantasies, said to be common in adults, seem to be rare in children. Our own clinical experience leads us to favour the view that sometimes the problem is initiated by a concern about being overweight, but that it becomes incorporated in complex family interactions, with the food-refusal serving various purposes, including detouring of conflict and covert rejection of the food-provider (usually the mother).

We consider it unlikely that all cases of anorexia nervosa have the same dynamics (or causes). Bruch (1973) has described different types of the condition, and, given the increasing publicity and 'popularity' we can expect yet more variations.

Management

It is not surprising, given the multitudinous explanations for causation, that there should also be considerable variations in views on treatment. Predictably, analytical schools recommend individual psychotherapy or psychoanalysis, despite the fact that this approach has proved singularly ineffective (Tolstrup 1975). Bruch is also scathing of the enthusiastic and optimistic behaviour modifiers (for example Blinder, Freeman, and Stunkard 1970), noting that though initial weight-gain is impressive, follow-up indicates a downhill course. Family therapists are the latest group to make claims for the effectiveness of their methods. Minuchin, Rosman, and Baker (1978) work on the basis that some families have certain characteristics which encourage the development of psychosomatic illness in a child, whilst the physiological vulnerability of the child determines which illness it may be. The treatment is then focused on helping the family change their specific transactional characteristics to free the sick child from his special role (see Chapter 5). Of particular interest is the description of the 'diagnostic family meal' in which the therapist sits in with the family at a meal, as a way of capturing the conflict about eating in the session, and thus making both the symptom and the conflict available to direct intervention.

Whatever one's theoretical orientation, it seems to us that there can be little doubt that treatment has two main aims: (1) correction of the weight-loss, and (2) resolution of the precipitating psychological causes. We recommend that both these be tackled from the beginning and in parallel. The weight-gain may be achieved by a variety of behavioural methods, or by hospitalization, and even if necessary, artificial feeding when life is threatened. Crisp (1977) describes a hospital-based programme incorporating graded reward-scheme for weight-gain, combined with individual psychotherapy. Minuchin, Rosman, and Baker (1978) consider hospitalization unnecessary, as they claim satisfactory weight-gain shortly after the 'diagnostic meal'.

It has been said that one should use the treatment with which one feels most comfortable. This is a debatable point, but it is probably what occurs in practice anyhow. In anorexia nervosa, there can be no doubt that unless both aims are achieved, the long-term outlook is poor. Follow-up studies (for example, Warren 1968) indicate something in the region of 65 per cent make a reasonable recovery, 25 per cent have significant disabling symptoms and up to 10 per cent die! In our view, it is essential to involve the family of the anorectic child, for the family undoubtedly plays a significant part in maintaining the problem.

(XII) DRUG MISUSE

Drug misuse in pre-adolescents is at present rare, but as the incidence increases in the adolescent population so it is spreading to younger children also. Commonly misused drugs amongst adolescents include tobacco, cannabis, alcohol, hallucinogens such as LSD, barbiturates and tranquillizers, amphetamines and opiates. The most recent vogue is for glue-sniffing, the effects of which can be similar to those of hallucinogens.

The causes of drug misuse are complex and multifactorial. They include social pressures, ready availability, and the individual's need to gain confidence, allay anxiety, satisfy curiosity, and conform to peer-group norms. There is no doubt that *all* the drugs listed are potentially harmful, and most of them are very dangerous indeed from a physical viewpoint. The potential for addiction exists with most drugs, and is accentuated by the emotional problems that pre-date the misuse of the drug.

Management must take into account such factors as the physical damage done by the drug, any physical or psychological dependence, the pre-existing emotional problems, and the family. The outlook is generally poor.

Ellis (1979) has reported a follow-up study of drug misuse. He attempts to identify a social profile of those who have taken drugs and continued to abuse them after an interval of abstinence in borstal. Poor predictive factors for hard-drug misuse include above-average intelligence, young age on arrival in borstal, early school-leaver, loss of father at an early age, supportive and understanding parents, and small families of origin. The only significant predictive factor for soft drugs is the poorer outlook for those whose parents take psychotropic medication.

Solvent abuse (glue-sniffing) is currently a major problem amongst adolescents. Solvents are readily available, cheap, and legal, and are therefore an easily obtainable alternative to alcohol or other drugs. They act by initially reducing consciousness, and thus producing disinhibition and elation. If sniffing continues, aggression, halluci-nations, and coma occur. Glue-sniffers tend to come from socially and psychologically disadvantaged families. There is as yet no concensus on how solvent-abuse should be managed. Masterton (1979) in his comprehensive review of the problem makes the novel recommendation that the parents should encourage the child to drink alcohol in the home as a replacement, on the premise that prohibition rarely works, but that substitution therapy is of value in drug misuse. This is a very debatable view and we prefer treatment to be focused on the cause of the problem.

(XIII)   SEXUAL DISORDERS

In considering sexual disorders, an understanding of normal psycho-sexual development is essential. The reader is referred to Rutter (1971) for a clear description of this complicated topic. It is important to differentiate between what is developmentally normal behaviour and what is clearly abnormal. For example, masturbation is almost universal, and mutual masturbation between children of the same sex is far more common than some people would wish to admit. Homosexual attachments are common in adolescence, especially in sexually segregated schools, and have no significance in terms of persisting adult homosexuality, the causes of which are highly complex (see Bancroft 1968, Kenyon 1970).

Disorders of psychosexual identity occur in pre-adolescents as well as in older age-groups. The child may .insist on dressing like a member of the opposite sex, and may identify with the behaviour and appearance of the opposite sex. The commonest form is feminism in boys. Frequently in such situations, the parents have wished for a child of the opposite sex, and have unconsciously, or otherwise, encouraged such behaviour accordingly.

Management

The family will require help in recognizing and modifying their contribution to the problem, as well as in promoting an improved self-image in the child and a stronger identification with others of his own sex. The more severely disturbed child may benefit from additional individual psychotherapy.

(XIV) ADJUSTMENT REACTIONS

These are mild and transient disorders, usually occurring in previously normal children, as a response to an obvious stress such as change of school or loss of a pet. The problem may take any form, for example, withdrawal, tics, bed-wetting, or sullenness. It is sufficiently mild and short-lived not to be deemed a psychiatric disorder, and not require any specific treatment other than an explanation to and reassurance for the parents and teachers, with advice on how to help the child work through his distress.

(XV) THE ABUSED CHILD

The exact incidence of child abuse is not known because so many cases are not proven and probably many are not even suspected. Studies indicate an incidence of 1–12 in 1000 (Scott 1977). Child abuse may take many forms – the most well recognized is *non-*

accidental injury in which physical injury is inflicted upon the child. The child may have bruises, burns, or fractures, and the parents usually either deny any knowledge of the cause or offer alternative and often unlikely explanations.

There are other, less well-recognized forms of child abuse. Rogers *et al.* (1976) have described a number of cases of *non-accidental poisoning* in which the children have been admitted to hospital with serious medical problems. Intensive investigation reveals no obvious cause, and the possibility of poisoning is then considered. Occasionally under such circumstances, the child has an onset of symptoms such as vomiting, diarrhoea, fits, or more bizarre symptoms after a parental visit. The incidence of poisoning is not known but since Rogers' paper we have been involved with several cases. Death in childhood by non-accidental poisoning has been documented.

Other forms of child abuse include *neglect* in which the child may be dirty, poorly clothed, malnourished, developmentally delayed, and emotionally disturbed, and *emotional abuse* in which the child suffers from long-term and persistent exposure to hostility and resentment, or extreme over-protection and over-involvement, with subsequent severe damage to his psychological and possibly physical development. Mrazek (1980) has described the different forms of *sexual abuse* in childhood.

The causes of child abuse are complex. Gelles (1973) argues the importance of a multi-dimensional approach focusing on sociological, psychological, and contextual variables. Lynch (1975) identifies six factors which occur significantly more often than others: an abnormal pregnancy, an abnormal labour or delivery, neonatal separation, further separations in the first 6 months of life, and illnesses in the first year of life in both the baby and the mother. Green, Gaines, and Sandgrund (1974) consider child abuse to be the end result of three potentiating factors: the abuse-prone personality of the parent, characteristics of the child that predispose him to scapegoating, and current environmental stress. They also note that role reversal is a prominent feature in the psychodynamic make-up of such families, and that the parents tend to endow the child with negative characteristics derived from their own experience with rejecting parents. Most authorities refer to the presence of marital conflict, and environmental stresses such as overcrowding, financial difficulties, and lack of support, seem to be of particular importance.

Speight, Bridson, and Cooper (1979) have reported on the follow-up of fifty-nine cases of child abuse, two to four years after the episode. All children had been returned to their families, eighteen with no legal sanctions, and forty-one with legal sanctions. There were five repeat episodes in the first group and four in the second. In addition, in five cases the initial episode of abuse had been preceded by serious abuse of a sibling. Thus, in fourteen cases out of fifty-nine, an episode of child abuse occurred which was potentially preventable. The authors conclude that psycho-social assessments of these families were too superficial and that workers were erring on the side of over-optimism in their view of families. Serious permanent physical damage occurs in over 25 per cent of cases (Scott 1977). The adverse emotional consequences are beyond measurement, but undoubtedly abused children become abusing parents.

Management

The management of child abuse calls for a most carefully co-ordinated and comprehensive approach, using the full range of therapeutic and practical facilities. Far too often management consists of case conferences and casework without clearly defined short or long-term goals. A policy of 'wait and see' or 'give them another chance' is insufficient, even when supported by an at-risk register, regular case conferences, and frequent visits.

It has been argued that the first necessity is to obtain legal sanctions in all cases unless the family situation is unusually favourable (Speight, Bridson, and Cooper 1979). Some may disagree with this, but whether or not such a policy is adopted there can be no doubt that a determined and authoritative approach is essential. A decision must be made with regard to the child's future as soon as possible. If the child is to return to his natural family then intensive and early work with the family is required. The aims of this work include the modification of those factors which interact to precipitate the episode. Such work is of a long-term nature and necessitates the use of a worker who is not likely to be leaving in the foreseeable future. It may take many months to engage the family and years to help such parents gain insight into, for example, the intrusion of the past into their current relationship with the child. Change will occur only during a period of years.

As a complementary measure, Reavley and Gilbert (1976) recommend the use of a careful behavioural analysis (see Chapter 8) of the events leading up to the episode of abuse. Specific triggering factors such as prolonged crying may be identified. Behavioural treatment is then focused on response prevention, and promotion of new coping behaviour. The abused child may well require individual psychotherapeutic help to overcome feelings of confusion, guilt, anger, and sadness.

It may be necessary to make use of a wide range of practical facilities such as nursery schools, day-centres, home-helps, re-housing, and financial aid to overcome the environmental stresses. Many cases of abuse occur outside 'office hours' and parents should be advised of organizations such as Parents Anonymous, and helped to find an appropriate network of support.

If long-term placement away from the family is considered necessary then adoption or long-term fostering should be the goal. Such children urgently need to form new attachment bonds in a secure family setting, away from the damaging effects of both their own families and of institutions. Social workers are too often over-optimistic about the possibility of altering severe personality disturbances in the parents, unaware of the urgency of early placement, and reluctant to break family ties. Children who are placed away from home will need individual therapy to cope with all the feelings discussed above, as well as with the loss of their family and their resentment to those responsible for their separation.

Preventive measures include the recognition of the 'at risk' family and the provision of support and guidance to help overcome the cumulative effect of a multitude of predisposing factors. In particular, attempts must be made to enhance bonding in those situations where it is threatened, such as repeated illness or separation, and to help parents under stress develop more adaptive coping mechanisms.

Diagnostic categories (5) – developmental problems

Introduction

Some children have a specific difficulty in acquiring skills such as reading, co-ordination, or speech, despite being of normal intelligence and experiencing a normal environment. The term 'specific developmental delay' is often used, but can be rather misleading. Its use means that there is no primary explanation for the delay. The children are not intellectually retarded, they have no major environmental problems, and they are receiving normal education. The term 'primary developmental problem' would be more accurate.

Occasionally, there is a family history of such difficulties and boys are affected more often than girls, suggesting that there is an inherited biological cause.

(1) SPECIFIC READING DELAY

Such children have a serious impairment in the development of reading or spelling skills, despite being of normal intelligence, and receiving adequate education. Occasionally, there may be associated difficulties with the development of speech and language. The term 'dyslexia' has been used to describe such problems, and is of value if it is used to pinpoint a specific reading delay which requires skilled remedial help. However, it has the disadvantage of often being used to describe all children who have trouble reading. The true causes of reading difficulties are as yet unknown, though there are likely to be multiple factors involved, both past and present, in the child and his environment (Rutter 1975). The incidence of specific reading delay was about 1 in 10 in a study of 10 year-olds in Inner London (Berger, Yule, and Rutter 1975). Boys are affected three times more often than girls.

The sequelae of reading retardation include falling behind in other lessons, poor self-image, and consequent behaviour problems. There is a strong association between reading delay and anti-social behaviour problems. Untreated, there is progressive failure at school, and spelling and writing problems in adult life.

Treatment requires skilled remedial help, which may be provided in individual or group settings. The teacher uses structured techniques that ensure frequent success to boost the child's confidence. Attention should be paid to any additional environmental problems, and careful explanations should be given to parents, who may consider their child to be lazy or retarded.

Similar problems may relate to a specific arithmetical delay.

(ii)   DEVELOPMENTAL SPEECH OR LANGUAGE DELAY

For the normal development of language, and therefore speech, the infant requires a certain degree of brain maturation, the ability to hear, a satisfying emotional environment, and adequate stimulation. A delay or defect in the development of speech may be due to such organic factors as brain damage or dysfunction (p. 78), autism (pp. 67–8), mental retardation, or deafness. Psychological causes include emotional deprivation and stimulus deprivation. Occasionally, no cause can be found for a child's failure to develop speech. Under such circumstances, the condition is known as specific language delay (or dysphasia or aphasia). Such states are very handicapping, and the child requires highly specialized help in developing the use of language and other learning skills. His frustration may be expressed through behaviour problems. His parents require extra help to understand the nature of the problem, and to assist the child in his development, as well as coping with the behaviour difficulties and their own distress. The outlook in these specific conditions is often poor. There is an association for such children – AFASIC (Association for All Speech Impaired Children, London).

None of the above conditions should be confused with elective mutism, the nature of which is totally different (p. 62).

(iii)   UNDERACHIEVEMENT

One of the most common reasons for referral of a child for child guidance is underachievement. The concept of underachievement is complex and many of the potential causes have already been discussed. The most obvious causes are in cases of intellectual or mental retardation and specific learning difficulties (p. 90). However, there is another group of children who are of normal intellect, who have no *specific* areas of difficulty in learning and who have often made substantial early progress at school, but who later fail to make further progress. In these children, there are usually important emotional causes for their difficulties. They may lack motivation, be anxious, frightened, or unhappy.

Any underachieving child requires a detailed assessment of his intellectual capacity, emotional state, and family background. Any obvious causes should be remedied where possible. Such children require remedial help at school and the sympathetic understanding of teachers and parents. Contributing environmental factors such as family stresses should also be tackled.

(IV) THE GIFTED CHILD

There is no clear definition of 'gifted', and, indeed, many child psychiatrists and psychologists are critical of the concept. Nonetheless, some children have IQs of 140 or more, and do seem to have emotional or, paradoxically, learning problems. The parent or teacher may observe that the child is aloof, disinterested, bored, failing to learn, or experiencing difficulty with relationships. Such children easily become bored at school, because of insufficient stimulation, and then 'switch-off', and even fall behind. They may be teased by other children because they are 'different', and become socially isolated. Often they fail to make friends, stating that they find the company of other children boring. A careful assessment, including intelligence-testing reveals the cause of the difficulties. Management is aimed at providing a stimulating educational environment so that the child becomes more involved and interested in his work. There is an Association for Gifted Children, which provides support groups, activity holidays, etc. (National Association for Gifted Children, London).

5

Family and marital therapy

Introduction

The fundamental philosophy of family therapy was first expressed by
John Donne 400 years ago: 'No man is an island, entire of itself; every
man is a piece of the Continent, a part of the main.' The conceptual
focus is on the family system as a whole – individual behaviour is seen
as arising from and feeding back into the whole family system.

Family therapy should be distinguished from 'family casework', in
which 'the focus is on the behaviour of individuals' (Sussenwein
1976: 980), and 'the family is used instrumentally as a means of
assisting change within individual family members' (Walrond-
Skinner 1976: 5). In family therapy the focus is on the whole family
system, and interventions are aimed at altering the *whole* system.
Marital therapy may be considered as a particular form of family
therapy in which the focus is on the marital dyad. The basic
principles underlying the theory and practice of family therapy are
generally applicable to marital therapy, and to avoid unnecessary
repetition we use only the term family therapy unless specifically
stated otherwise.

In this chapter, we outline the theoretical orientations most influential to family therapy, and we describe the dimensions along which
family therapy is practised. We describe our own approach to family
therapy and, with illustrations, discuss the techniques we find useful.
The process cannot be taught in one chapter nor even in a whole
book. The student can only learn by doing. He is best taught by live

supervision, video tapes, and the observation of skilled therapists in action.

One of the major criticisms of the psychotherapies has been the lack of evaluative research. If the number of papers published reviewing evaluative research for a particular therapy may be used as an indicator of the amount of research carried out, then family therapy is well represented. In the last ten years there have been over forty reviews of family therapy outcome research. One recent extensive review of current research into the effectiveness of family therapy indicates that therapeutic optimism is justified (Gurman and Kniskern 1979). We believe that family therapy is potentially the most effective way of helping children and adults with behavioural and emotional problems, and that it warrants detailed consideration by all social workers.

Theoretical considerations

Although there is no single universally accepted theory of family functioning, the unifying theory underlying the current practice of family therapy is the conceptualization of the family as an interacting system. Within the overall framework of family therapy, four major theoretical orientations are represented.

(i) PSYCHOANALYTIC THEORY

Many of the pioneers of family therapy operated within a psychoanalytic framework, applying psychoanalytic theory to the family as a whole (e.g. Ackerman 1966, Bowen 1966, Paul 1967). In Britain today some of the leading family therapists attempt to integrate the psychoanalytic and family systems framework (e.g. Skynner 1976, Bentovim 1979, Byng-Hall 1979, Dare 1979). Dare suggests that psychoanalytic thinking can make crucial contributions to formulation of the family using three frames of reference, (i) the life-cycle of the family, (ii) the historical intergenerational structure of the family, and (iii) the interactional structure of the family. With these frames of reference a full picture may be obtained of the family as an evolving, historical, and current structure.

In questioning whether the psychoanalytic framework, which is essentially individual oriented, may be integrated into the framework of the family system, Walrond-Skinner (1976: 23) comments on various 'irreconcilable points of difference', but concludes that at least three psychoanalytic concepts are applicable to the understanding and treatment of families, (i) family myths (Byng-Hall 1979), (ii) intrafamilial transference distortions (Barnes 1973), and (iii) interlocking pathology (Framo 1970: 127).

One of the most convincing and clearly explained integrations of psychoanalytic and family-systems frameworks is that of Lieberman (1980) who postulates a transgenerational theory and therapy. This transgenerational approach focuses on the dimension of time within the family system – it attempts to understand the present through the use of the past so as to plan and catalyse a new future.

(ii)   COMMUNICATIONS THEORY

Communication has been defined as 'how the system's components interact' (Walrond-Skinner 1976: 17). The communication theorists would consider a poorly functioning family to be one in which the communication patterns are faulty. Walrond-Skinner has described three forms of dysfunctional communication.

(i)   'Blocked' communication includes prolonged silence, withdrawal or isolation, and the existence of family secrets.

(ii)   'Displaced' communication refers to the use of symptoms as a form of interpersonal message. The quality and carrier of the symptom represent significant forms of communication. For example, the child who soils himself each time his parents have a row is expressing in a displaced way his distress at the parental friction.

(iii)   'Damaged' communication – every communicated message has two levels, the content of the message and the way in which the message is conveyed (i.e. the metacommunication). In healthy communication, these two levels are congruent, but where they lack congruence the communication is damaged, e.g. a mother asks her child to kiss her whilst conveying, non-verbally, anger, or resentment. The effect of such pairs of communication being repeated over a prolonged period of time can be confusion, despair, and ultimately withdrawal. This pattern has been postulated to be of causative significance in schizophrenia by

Bateson and his colleagues (1956) who used the term 'double-bind'.

The most influential of the communication school family therapists have been Jackson (1968), Haley (1976), Watzlawick and Weakland (1977), and Satir (1978).

(III) STRUCTURAL THEORY

A family is a system that operates through transactional patterns. Repeated transactions establish patterns of how, when, and to whom to relate, and these patterns underpin the system (Minuchin 1974: 51). The structural family therapist considers these repeated transactional patterns along two main dimensions, cohesiveness, and adaptability. He emphasizes their importance in the context of the family as a whole and in the sub-systems of the family, i.e. one or more individuals drawn together by generation, sex, interest, or function. Thus there is a parental sub-system, a sibling sub-system, a male sub-system, etc.

Cohesiveness refers to the boundaries between sub-systems. A boundary is a rule defining who participates in the sub-system, and how. The degree of permeability of these boundaries is a useful index of family functioning. In some families the boundaries are excessively permeable, or diffuse; such families (known as 'enmeshed') are characterized by over-responsiveness, lack of differentiation, excessive concern and communication. If a child in such a family announces, for example, that he has a tummy-ache, there is an immediate and intense reaction from one or more individuals with excessive concern expressed. In other families the boundaries are rigid or impermeable. Families with rigid boundaries (known as 'disengaged') tend to be unresponsive, apathetic and poor communicators. A child with a tummy-ache in a disengaged family may be completely ignored. Well-functioning families tend to have 'semi-permeable' boundaries.

Adaptability refers to the ability of the family and its sub-systems to adjust to changed circumstances. A well-functioning or 'flexible' family is able to adjust to major life-changes, or interruptions such as illness or other specific stresses. Some families are 'rigid', i.e. unable to adjust or adapt, whilst others are over-flexible to the point of being 'chaotic'. The 'rigid' family finds it difficult to allow an adolescent any age-appropriate autonomy, whereas the 'chaotic' family allows the adolescent too much autonomy, asserting no controls over him.

The structural approach, the leading exponent of which is Minuchin (1974), enjoys considerable popularity in Britain at present.

(iv) LEARNING THEORY

The traditional application of learning theory to the understanding and treatment of individuals has in the last ten years or so been extended to families, e.g. Liberman (1970), Alexander and Parsons (1973), Crowe (1973), Levere and Kirk (1979). Douglas (1979) notes two major trends in behavioural work with families, (i) a 'triadic' model of therapy where the 'patient' (child) is treated by the therapist through a mediator (parent), (ii) learning theory is applied to the understanding and modification of family communication and interaction patterns. Behavioural techniques are used to modify the symptoms whilst family therapy concentrates on enabling the family to accept the changes within the child, and realign relationships within the family that will allow the child to remain symptom-free.

Levere and Kirk (1979) provide a helpful description of a combined therapeutic approach in a family setting.

Practical considerations

Within the context of family therapy there is considerable overlap in the application of theoretical knowledge and there are a wide variety of therapeutic interventions in common use. Various authors have tried to make sense of a bewildering array of approaches by describing different dimensions along which family therapists practise (Madanes and Haley 1977, Lieberman 1980: 17). We consider below the most important of these dimensions.

(a) *Theoretical orientation.* We have discussed this dimension above. The practice of family therapy may be based on, for example, purely behavioural or psychoanalytic principles.

(b) *Activity.* Therapists may be active, directive, and controlling at one extreme, or passive, non-directive, and interpretive at the other.

Beels and Ferber (1969) have classified well-known therapists along this dimension as 'conductors', 'reactors' or 'systems-purists'.

(c) Past or present.   Therapists differ on whether the emphasis should be on the past or the present. Some prefer the traditional psycho-dynamic approach of focusing on the past as a means of both under-standing the cause of the problem, and finding solutions (e.g. Ackerman 1966, Dicks 1967, Boszormenyi-Nagy and Spark 1973). Others prefer to concentrate on current interaction on the assump-tion that this plays an important part in maintaining the problem, whatever its cause (e.g. Minuchin 1974, Haley 1976, Satir 1978). Some British therapists are working towards an integration (e.g. Bentovim 1979, Dare 1979).

(d) Goals of therapy.   Some therapists define the goals of therapy as alleviation of the presenting symptoms (e.g. Patterson 1971) whilst others focus upon the growth and development of the whole family (e.g. Bowen 1971, Minuchin 1974, Satir 1978).

(e) Flexibility.   This dimension relates to the freedom of the therapist to adapt his way of working to the particular family he is treating. Some therapists prefer to use the same set of procedures and tech-niques for every family for example, whilst others design a specific procedure for each family and problem, tending to change what they are doing if it is not succeeding (e.g. Haley 1976, Watzlawick, Weakland, and Fisch 1974).

A frame of reference

From the preceding descriptions, it can be seen that family therapy is an evolving treatment which draws upon different theoretical and practical orientations. Each therapist brings to therapy his own personality, imagination, sense of humour, and ability to share other's emotions (Andolfi 1979). These are as important as his own theoretical standpoint and technical expertise. We believe that family therapy should be based upon a clearly defined frame of reference for the understanding of a family's difficulties and the planning of strategies designed to help overcome them. Our own framework is presented as a series of carefully considered aspects.

Formulation
Agreement with the family
Members of family who attend.
Interval between sessions
Length of sessions
Years, months, or weeks of therapy?

Therapeutic goals
How to intervene
Evaluation of progress
Responsibility of the family
Authority of the therapist
Persistence
Indications and contraindications
Supervision
Termination of therapy.

(We hope that the fact that the initial letters of each item creates the mnemonic FAMILY THERAPIST will assist rather than distract the reader!)

FORMULATION

A formulation in family terms as described in Chapter 3 is mandatory. It should seek to answer the questions – what is happening, what is maintaining it, what constitutes positive change, and how may this be achieved? The formulation may be unclear initially, and indeed may change from one session to the next, but without it the therapist is like an explorer with no compass.

AGREEMENT WITH THE FAMILY

Any attempt to help a family without its agreement is likely to fail. The therapist has to actively engage the family in a joint effort to understand and resolve its problems. It may take more than one family meeting to reach a working agreement but the therapist should ensure that he and the family have a 'therapeutic contract'. The components of this contract are discussed under the next five headings.

MEMBERS OF FAMILY WHO ATTEND

We prefer to work with the whole family, on the principle that the absence of one or more family members allows the creation of a false picture of the family, encourages one family member to speak for another, and impedes problem-solving. Certainly there are occasions when it is appropriate to work with specific sub-systems, such as during the discussion of serious marital difficulties, including sexual problems, when just the parents would attend, or as a specific strategy where, for example, the therapist might invite just the father and adolescent son for a couple of sessions if he wanted to explore and/or strengthen their relationship.

In general, we consider the whole family to be all those members of the family living under the same roof, but it is often appropriate to invite members of the extended family as well, especially when they are involved in the difficulties.

INTERVAL BETWEEN SESSIONS

A balance has to be found between maintaining the momentum of therapy and allowing the family sufficient time to integrate the content of the sessions. Most therapists find a fortnightly meeting quite satisfactory. Occasionally it may be necessary to meet more frequently when, for example, a family is in crisis, or less frequently when there are very real practical difficulties associated with attending.

LENGTH OF SESSIONS

The content and process of family meetings is normally so rich and complex that it is advisable to ensure there is plenty of time available. Forty-five minutes is probably an absolute minimum in which useful work may be done, and two hours is as much as most families and therapists can be expected to tolerate. Once the length of the sessions has been agreed the therapist should ensure the session ends on time. In this way the family begins to introduce important issues early in sessions when they can be dealt with more effectively than at the end. Further, the therapist who sticks to the time-limit has a clear idea of the pacing and structure of the session. He should not take up important issues at the end when he is likely to feel satiated and concerned about his next appointment. The best way to ensure a session ends on time is to start concluding it at least ten minutes before the scheduled ending, thus allowing the family time to work through immediate issues. We make a point of saying, 'We have to stop in ten minutes'.

YEARS, MONTHS OR WEEKS?

It is not possible to determine in advance how many sessions may be required to help a family find solutions to its problems. Nonetheless, we find it useful to decide in advance with the family on an initial number of meetings. This encourages us to work with some urgency and to evaluate our progress, and it discourages a sense of lethargy, and, for the family, dependence. We usually offer six sessions initially – this allows sufficient time for most families to initiate or consolidate change. With other families it may require six sessions to gain a clear understanding of the problem. A new contract can be negotiated when necessary.

THERAPEUTIC GOALS

The first goal of any therapeutic contract must be the redefinition of the presenting problem in terms of the family relationships.

The parents of Sheila, 12, sought help because she had suffered recurrent abdominal pains for several months. Her mother was a very anxious person who could not tolerate being alone, and her father was a shift-worker, doing a lot of overtime, who had little sympathy for his wife. It was clear both to the referring doctor and to the therapist that Sheila's pains were not physically determined, and that they served the purpose of keeping her away from school. For the parents the pain was a point of contact – it was something they could worry about together and do something about together. They unconsciously encouraged it. Further, it allowed Sheila's mother to have Sheila at home with her as a substitute for her peripheral husband.

For the therapist the first goal is to help the family understand the abdominal pain as a communication from the child that all is not well in the family. Once the family accepts the re-framing the therapist can then explore with the family his hypothesis that the parents are detouring an unresolved conflict via their daughter. If the hypothesis proves correct, the next goal would be the exploration of the conflict, and the search for alternative ways of handling and then hopefully resolving the conflict. If the hypothesis is incorrect, the goal is the search for an alternative explanation for the family dysfunction. It is essential to have the family's co-operation in each step. Without it, progress is very difficult and the family is likely to become confused, resistant, antagonistic, and eventually absent!

Succeeding goals are determined by the quality of the family dysfunction. They may include the restructuring of dysfunctional relationships, the improved communication of thoughts and feelings, or the search for alternative ways of solving problems, resolving conflict, reaching decisions, or coping with major changes in the family life-cycle. It is important that both the therapist and the family should be clear about each step. The goals should be clearly stated in terms of observable and concrete behaviour. They should be simple and obtainable for change is more easily obtained when goals are small.

HOW TO INTERVENE

Once the therapeutic contract has been agreed and the goals of therapy are defined, the next phase begins. In general, the therapist should act as a catalyst of, and commentator on, family interaction. We encourage the family members to discuss together their problems, and we avoid being centralized by the family, i.e. put in the central position of communication, like a telephone switchboard. If the therapist is centralized he cannot objectively note all the complexities of the family relationships and he is more likely to take sides, make decisions for the family, etc. Most families attempt to centralize the therapist, and he must quickly teach them that he is more concerned with what, and how, they communicate to each other than to him.

We avoid concentrating too heavily on the detail of verbal content, and focus rather on the content of the interaction between family members, the 'process' of the family. By continuous encouragement of family interaction, we gradually elicit recurrent patterns of dysfunction. Once the quality of such patterns is clear, we can share our view of what is happening with the family, and seek its co-operation in finding alternative and more functional ways of relating.

We are now in a position to challenge dysfunctional sequences. If communication patterns are faulty we can assist the family to find more open, direct, and congruent ways of communicating. This involves a high degree of therapist activity. We stop interruptions and prevent one person speaking for another; we challenge in-congruence between verbal and non-verbal messages; we question communications that lack clarity or continuity; we disallow state-ments that disqualify or deny another's thoughts or feelings; we check that messages are being received and understood; we encourage the expression and sharing of feelings.

Where there are dysfunctional relationships, we attempt to help the family find healthier patterns of relating. Again, considerable therapist activity is necessary. We challenge inappropriate alliances or coalitions, we question scapegoating, myths, the validity of 'secrets', inappropriate rules and social stereotypes such as 'men don't cry', 'women prefer to be at home'. We encourage age-appropriate behaviour and autonomy, and clear boundaries between sub-systems. We assist families in the search for new ways to make decisions, solve problems, resolve conflicts, and adjust to change.

When progress is slow, other techniques may be of value. We may explore inter-generational issues as a way of understanding con-fusion, resistance, or distress. Tasks may be designed for the family to carry out, initially in the session, and later between sessions, so that it may practice new ways of relating or coping. Role-plays and role-reversals can be useful techniques for the development of insight and empathy. Sculpting – a non-verbal representation of family relation-ships (Andolfi 1979: 78–87) is of value for families who tend to intellectualize, or who are over-defended, or verbally impoverished.

The reader who is unfamiliar with all these active and challenging techniques of family therapy, may question the right of the therapist to take such a stance, and even impose his own values. He may wonder whether the family does not feel criticized by the constant challenging and checking. It is worth remembering that the therapist and the family have agreed to solve a problem together. So long as the therapist is able to convey his neutrality, empathy, and under-standing, he will be perceived as a reflector of the family problem, and a sounding-board for solutions. As we discuss later, the responsibility for change remains that of the family. It retains the right and indeed has the power to resist, providing the therapist does not abuse his own power, stemming from his knowledge and authority.

EVALUATION OF PROGRESS

In the complexity and excitement of the sessions it is all too easy to lose sight of the therapeutic goals. An important aspect of family therapy is the repeated evaluation of therapeutic progress, a sort of continuous assessment. This involves a frequent verification of what is happening in relation to the formulation and goals. Are we helping the family to work on the agreed focus? If so, what progress have we made? If the progress is satisfactory what further work is required? If progress is unsatisfactory or the agreed focus is being avoided, what is going wrong? Have we misunderstood the problem, is the family resisting our attempt to help, are we using the wrong strategies? We are bound to make mistakes, and families do often resist. What matters is that we recognize mistakes and resistance, and this we can only do by continuous evaluation of progress.

A family consisting of father, a bus driver in his 40s; mother, the same age; and David and John, aged 13 and 11, were referred because John was miserable, threatening to run away from home and under-achieving at school. In the first interview it was made clear that David had always been the more successful, and that there had always been much arguing between them. During the session, whatever one said the other contradicted. The initial formulation hypothesized that John's behaviour was a reaction to having lived in David's shadow, a problem exacerbated by John's recent entry into the same secondary school as David. The family agreed with this view and goals were defined which included increasing John's self-esteem by encouraging his strengths, and allowing him to be different from David.

Despite full co-operation from the family, there was no change in John's behaviour and the boys continued to squabble. On reviewing progress there was no evidence of resistance, and the strategies seemed correct. Was the initial formulation incomplete or incorrect? It did lack reference to the marital sub-system, and the therapist had observed during the sessions a paucity of contact between the parents, and yet the boys squabbled incessantly. A fresh hypothesis suggested that David and John were 'acting-out' marital dysharmony, with each son being allied to one parent against the other. The therapist tested out this hypothesis by asking the parents to discuss with each other one of the areas of dispute between the boys. The parents avoided this by allowing their sons to interrupt and take over the argument. When the therapist challenged this detouring behaviour, the parents were forced to face up to what proved to be severe difficulties in their own relationship. Their ready agreement with the initial formulation was part of their resistance. A new therapeutic contract of marital therapy was agreed, and the boys soon stopped arguing, and John quickly improved.

The 'why and how of evaluation', both during therapy and at follow-up are more fully discussed elsewhere (Lask 1980).

RESPONSIBILITY OF THE FAMILY

Many therapists of whatever orientation hold a sort of messianic belief that it is their responsibility to solve the client's problems. We believe this to be a potentially harmful myth, which has possibly arisen from some confusion between what the doctor does for his physically ill patient, and what the therapist might do for his client with emotional problems. There are major differences between potent physical treatments which can indeed relieve or cure serious organic problems, and the psychotherapeutic techniques used to help the client overcome his emotional difficulties. In family therapy the responsibility for change belongs not to the therapist but to the family. The therapist's task is to help the family find ways of changing.

The social worker spends considerable time helping families organize their lives, by sorting out housing problems, financial difficulties, legal issues, etc. If the worker takes too much responsibility for these rather than helping the families to do it for themselves, there is a danger that she might approach family therapy in the same way. The family can collude with this by investing the therapist with that responsibility. We must be wary of the unspoken – 'change the situation for us'.

A therapist was describing in a supervision group a particularly disorganized family with two young children aged 2½ and 1½, whom the immature parents could not control. He was asked to role-play a session. In the role-play he was trying to talk to the parents whilst the children caused chaos around them. He allowed the younger child to climb on his lap, and the elder to join in a game with him, as a way of trying to calm the situation. The effect of this was to prevent him from being able to help the family at this point because he had his own hands full.

The family therapist's task under such circumstances is to help the family find different and better ways of coping. He could have encouraged the parents to experiment with alternative methods until they found one that worked, or noticed what was going wrong, such as a lack of persistence or consistency on the parents' part. Minuchin, Rosman, and Baker (1978: 119–25) highlight this point in relation to the management of anorexia nervosa in children and adolescents. They advocate the use of a family meal in which the parents are encouraged to get the child to eat, as a way of demonstrating the family's dysfunctional relationships. The therapist does not accept the responsibility of getting the child to eat. The results are most impressive.

AUTHORITY

As family therapists we do not have the responsibility for change, but we do act as agents of change. 'We relate to the family initially as a consultant on their problems, and later a supervisor of their efforts' (Andolfi 1979: 13). We accept a request from a family to help it, and are thus invested with the authority to challenge the dysfunctional *status quo*. It has been argued that the use of authority, and indeed control, prevents the family from changing and growing, as if it is being kept in a state of child-like submission and dependency. Skynner (1976: 190) has argued that on the contrary, change and growth can only be achieved 'when there is something definite to react against'.

The therapist's use of self as an agent for change necessitates that we should have freedom of action, both physical, and emotional. We should be able to move about, control the pace and direction of the session, and fluctuate between active participation and passive observation. We should be able to share our feelings and check out the feelings of others. We must be able to challenge dysfunctional patterns of relating such as distorted communications, denials, and the wide range of resistances that families adopt. In a correctly negotiated therapeutic contract the therapist is invested with authority and must use it to be effective.

Statutory obligations

In situations where the social worker has real practical or statutory obligations to the family, she needs to make a clear distinction between the roles of family therapist and family supervisor during the therapy. Time should be set aside at the beginning of the session for discussion of any practical or legal issues. Once these have been discussed there should be no further reference to them during the session, and the therapist must politely but firmly stick to the agreed focus of therapy.

PERSISTENCE

Families usually present with a symptomatic member e.g. a child who soils, an anorectic adolescent, a psychotic parent, and implicitly or explicitly state: 'make this person better.' Often there is a secondary injunction, initially unstated, 'but don't ask us to change'. Families tread a delicate tightrope on the one side of which is the need to adapt to change (e.g. a child growing up) and on the other is the resistance to change, the homeostasis, or desire to retain the *status quo*. (Neither adaptation to change nor homeostasis are pathological, unless the former is so unrestrained that chaos ensues, or the latter so rigid that symptoms appear.) In resistant families, the therapist has to overcome the dilemma of being asked to effect change which at the same time the family resists. Under such circumstances, he has not only to insist that it is the family's responsibility to change, but he must use his authority to do this, and he must persevere in his efforts. He should be able to recognize the very wide variety of resistances that families adopt (Solomon 1969), and he should persist in his commenting upon, and challenging of such tactics. If he allows the family to outmanoeuvre him he has failed it.

Persistence is not the prerogative of the therapist. The family must also persevere. Sometimes a family will say they have tried everything and nothing works. The therapist may be able to help the family see that although it has tried everything it has persisted with nothing, and that failure has occurred through a lack of persistence and indeed consistency.

A particular school of therapy has arisen in response to very rigid and resistant families. Their 'paradoxical' approach is based upon the fact that 'every effort the therapist makes to change something will be boycotted on some levels, while on other levels the family will continue to seek help' (Andolfi 1979: 123). The paradoxical technique has some likeness to judo. The strength (resistance) of the opponent (family) is put to positive use. Paradoxical techniques depend for success on the family's defying the therapist's instructions, or following them to the point of absurdity and then recoiling. Their use is comprehensively discussed by, amongst others, Haley (1976) and Selvini Palazzoli and her colleagues (1978).

INDICATIONS AND CONTRA-INDICATIONS

Many family therapists have suggested selection criteria for family therapy. Some of the more comprehensive lists include those of Glick and Kessler (1974), Martin (1977), Bentovim (1978), and Walrond-Skinner (1978). The absence of a unifying language or classification system leads to considerable confusion, and the paucity of appropriate research encourages a dependency on clinical experience. In consequence, there is a fair amount of disagreement regarding which families are most likely to respond well to family therapy.

Our own view is based on our clinical experience and orientation, as well as some involvement in evaluative studies, and we accept that others may not agree with us. We consider that whatever the presenting problem the *assessment* should be of the whole family. The *treatment* should be of the family except when there are specific contra-indications: (a) refusal of one or more key members to attend, (b) inability of one or more key members to attend, (c) gross privation or deprivation experienced by the index client or other key family members, (d) a family in the process of breaking up and in which the parents are unwilling or unable to work together, (e) families in which one member is already receiving psychiatric help elsewhere (unless the liaison is very skilled). Under these circumstances, some form of individual oriented intervention is more likely to succeed. However, it should always be remembered that any intervention has an impact on the whole family, and the family continues to influence the individual. Occasionally, both an individual and family approach in parallel is indicated as, for example, with a child who has a serious problem with sexual identity.

The problem of working with poor, multi-problem, and unmotivated families is often raised. Minuchin et al. (1967) provide an excellent description of the successful treatment of such families. The same principles outlined in this chapter apply.

A decision to work with the whole family does not, of course, exclude working at times with sub-systems, such as the marriage, or even with individuals. Nor does it exclude the use of other techniques such as behaviour modification. The main consideration is that the presenting problem be understood in the context of the family system, and whatever the interventions used the results should be assessed in the same context.

SUPERVISION

The practice of both social work and family therapy includes a considerable emphasis on supervision. However, such conventional methods of supervision as process-recording do not lend themselves to the supervision of family therapy. The richness and complexity of sessions are difficult to convey, and it is for this reason that family therapists have developed different methods of supervision including audiotape, videotape, direct or 'live' supervision, and role-play techniques.

Audiotape aids the supervisory process by producing an accurate record of both the dialogue and the therapist's interventions. Videotape adds the visual dimension, the importance of which in family therapy cannot be overestimated. In addition, particular sequences can be re-played and analysed in detail. One-way screens are in more common use than video and are much cheaper to install. They allow for 'live' or direct supervision in which the supervisor watches the treatment session and supervisory instructions can be given directly in the therapy. Supervisor and supervisee may leave the room for discussion or communicate directly during the session.

Whilst initially this sounds threatening, it is generally agreed that some form of 'live' supervision is the most valuable, and therapists once used to it prefer this form of supervision to others. The combined use of video and live supervision allows for both retrospective and immediate supervision, and provides the best of both worlds. Families do not seem to react adversely to the use of technical equipment, observers, supervisors, or the interruption of sessions. Indeed, they are often impressed by these efforts to help them. Reservations that workers may have about imposing such innovations upon their clients for fear of their clients' reactions are more likely to be projections of the worker.

Papp (1980) has described the use of a supervisory team behind a one-way screen, the views of which are conveyed to the family as part of the strategy of therapy, and Olson and Pegg (1979) have outlined the use of a supervisory team actually sitting-in on the therapy in the context of a training programme in which one-way screens were unavailable.

Role-play techniques can be of value in training as well as therapy. The members of the supervision group role-play the family, so that a clearer understanding of the family dynamics may be gained. The therapist can also use the role-play to practice different forms of intervention.

Although these techniques have developed in response to the special needs of family therapy, their use would seem to be of value in the supervision of most forms of therapy. Indeed, in training workshops and on many courses designed to enhance therapeutic skills, audio-visual aids and action techniques are gaining considerable popularity.

A comment on *co-therapy* is required in this section, as its use has arisen more for the security of the therapists than for the benefit of the family. Undoubtedly, co-therapy has potential value if it does indeed increase the confidence of the therapists, and if they are able to make use of the more detailed observations that two can make. It is also possible for co-therapists to model a relationship in which problems can be shared and disagreements resolved constructively. However, there is a danger that co-therapy may complicate rather than ease the task. The potential advantages of co-therapy are dependent upon the pair's ability to be completely open and honest with each other at all times. If co-therapy is simply a matter of the blind leading the blind, then it would be better for the blind to use a stick or a dog. In general, we favour the use of one therapist who ensures he has adequate supervision.

Mills (1979) has described a useful variation of co-therapy for families who are receiving help from two agencies, in which workers from each agency combine to promote effective liaison.

TERMINATION OF THERAPY

Termination should be linked with the therapeutic contract. If the therapeutic goals have been reached, or if they are being worked towards, and the family has learned to work constructively on their problems, it is time to stop. Should family problems persist and goals remain unachieved, the therapist should decide whether to negotiate a further contract, have a period without therapy and review the situation later, or end the therapy regardless. A definite decision one way or another is far more constructive than a sort of endless dragging-on.

In general, there are fewer problems about terminating family as opposed to individual therapy. Because the family therapist focuses on the family's own relationships rather than its relationship with him, dependence and other 'transference' phenomena are less marked. On the whole, they are contained within the family.

Families may themselves choose to terminate therapy either because there has been a genuine improvement, or as a way of avoiding having to face up to painful issues. In the latter situation, the therapist may question this decision and even interpret it but ultimately must accept the family's autonomy. When families are in dispute, and one key member wants to stop, whilst others do not, the therapist should leave the decision to the family. It may be helpful, however, to link the disagreement to other areas of conflict, and so define the dispute about termination as but another example of the family's inability to work together and resolve conflict. If one or more members insist on stopping then their wish must be respected.

Case illustration

We use this case example to illustrate many of the different aspects of our frame of reference.

Danny, aged 14, was referred because of his parents' concerns regarding his unhappiness, lack of interest in anything, poor achievement at school, and isolation. He had a sister, Elaine, aged 11, and his parents were tired and dissatisfied people, whose lives revolved around caring for the maternal grandparents who lived nearby and who made many demands upon them. Father was a labourer who was not as successful in life as his wife would have liked. He had no contact with his own family for whom he had no respect or affection following an unhappy childhood. Mother was an only child who had never really been able to separate from her demanding parents. The family agreed that she was now doing the same thing to Danny, not allowing him any individuation, to the extent of standing next to him whilst he washed, insisting that she choose which clothes he wore each day, and that he (and Elaine) spend the weekends at her parents with her.

The initial *formulation* stated that Danny's behaviour was a response to the inappropriate demands made of him by his mother, who, in turn, had not been able to separate from her own parents. Father's inability to insist that the family lead its own life reinforced the problem, and led to his own withdrawal and dissatisfaction with ensuing marital disappointment and tension. This exacerbated the existing problems and encouraged mother to spend yet more time with her parents. The vicious cycle was complete.

An *agreement* with the family to work on these problems together was reached without too much difficulty, although mother expressed some doubt about the accuracy of the formulation. The therapeutic contract stipulated that all four *members of the family* would attend at fortnightly *intervals*, for sessions of fifty minutes' *length*. A *three-month* period of therapy was considered appropriate in the first instance. The *therapeutic goals* included Danny's individuation, increased involvement of Danny and father which would aid Danny's separation from his mother, and was anyhow more age-appropriate, increased contact and improved communication between the parents, and a reduction of the family's involvement with the grandparents.

The therapeutic goals gave clues about *how to intervene*. The family was asked to explore different ways of aiding Danny's independence. Danny and Elaine had a lively discussion, and one suggestion which the family adopted was that mother would leave Danny to wash himself and choose his own clothes. The therapist advised father to help mother allow this by chatting with her about other things at those times. In this way, another goal – that of increased contact between the parents – was worked towards. Mother initially resisted another suggestion, from all the others, that they should visit the grand-parents only on alternate weekends. The therapist encouraged father to try and help his wife express and understand the difficulty she had in coping with the suggestion. She talked about the resentment her own mother would feel, and her feeling that in some way she would be letting down her parents. The therapist challenged this resistance by asking the family to discuss how it felt about mother putting her parents first. They found this understandably difficult, and the therapist then suggested to father that he was old enough to make his own decisions, and maybe it was time he stood up to his in-laws. The children enjoyed this challenge and made a variety of suggestions of how they could spend the weekend together. Elaine volunteered that 'even going to watch West Ham with Danny and Dad would be more fun than going to my grandparents'.

Over a period of two or three sessions, many of the suggestions were put into effect. *Evaluation of progress* halfway through the contract showed that Danny had become happier and livelier, and was spend-ing short periods alone with father. The family only visited the grand-parents on alternate weekends, and spent the other weekends going out on trips. Mother still complained of Danny's lack of enthusiasm but had allowed him more autonomy. One task that had not been fulfilled was that of the parents spending a regular time alone together. When the therapist questioned this, it was clear that father was not fulfilling his side of the agreement. Indeed the *resistance* was much more his, than, as had been anticipated, his wife's. She remained sceptical but accepted the therapist's *authority* and always did what was suggested and agreed. The therapist had to use his authority and *persistence* to encourage father to complete the tasks. For example, it was agreed that after the children had gone to bed, father would make mother a cup of tea, and they would sit and chat. For several weeks he made the tea but then watched television. The therapist persevered in challenging this failure to comply, and eventually, much to mother's delight, father switched off the tele-vision. At this stage, it became clear that father's resistance had served to protect him from having to take an active part in communi-cating with his wife. They both expressed disappointment in the other.

The therapist decided to have a couple of sessions with the parents alone to help them explore the reasons for their mutual disappointment. A whole-family approach which had been *indicated* to this stage was now *contra-indicated* by the need of the parents to discuss matters which they would have been unable to do in front of the children. The therapist was moderately experienced and was not using *supervision* for this family, but members of the team were observing through the one-way screen. One observer felt that at this stage some case-work for the mother was indicated as the therapy had led to the loss of close relationships with both her son and her parents, and that'she required help to cope with these losses. The therapist insisted, however, that it was the husband's job to help her cope, and that his inadequacy may have reinforced her over-closeness to Danny and her parents.

The couple used the sessions constructively and started working out how they might improve their relationship. The therapist saw the family once more at the end of the contract. The next weekend the parents had arranged to go to a concert together, and leave the children at home. The situation seemed to have improved considerably. The therapist considered that this was the correct time to terminate therapy. The family had achieved all the therapeutic goals.

Follow-up six months later showed all the changes had been maintained. The therapist had not met the grandparents at any time because they refused to come. Although the grandmother had still from time to time expressed some resentment at the changes, there were no reported adverse effects.

Conclusions

Family therapy is a clinical orientation as well as a treatment technique. It draws upon a wide variety of theories and methods of practice. It is not an easy technique to learn, and yet when practised well, it can be very effective. The family therapist needs a clear frame of reference upon which to base his therapy, and we have offered our own as a guide. In Britain family therapy is very widely practised, and particularly by social workers. Despite this many social workers are based in agencies that may not have suitable facilities to see whole families, let alone all the technical equipment that some therapists use. Others are based in agencies where the practice of family therapy is not encouraged. Social workers who wish to gain skills and experience in family therapy should negotiate with their agency for the provision of appropriate resources and supervision. Where these are not forthcoming (and however experienced a senior may be she cannot supervise family therapy unless she has had a training herself), access may be gained to training courses such as those organized by the Institute of Family Therapy (London) or the Family Institute, Cardiff. The Association for Family Therapy has a nationwide network of local support groups.

6

Individual casework, counselling, and individual psychotherapy

Introduction

This chapter considers casework, counselling, and psychotherapy and their use with individuals. Until recently, these three methods of working have formed the hard core of the help offered in the child guidance clinic, and casework and counselling have also played an important role in the community-based service. As we advocate a family, rather than an individual approach to problems, it is inevitable that we consider these methods to have been over-used. However, there is a definite place for them, and in this chapter we discuss their special application to child-focused problems.

Individual casework and counselling

DEFINITIONS

There have been many attempts to present an overall theory of case-work or to define its special characteristics but these have often resulted in conceptual chaos (Sussenwein 1976). In addition to this, the terms casework, counselling (and sometimes psychotherapy) have been used interchangeably. It is probable that each client and worker has his own ideas about what these methods involve (Sutton 1979). We consider counselling to be a sort of casework which usually has some special focus, for example, counselling the parents of a mentally retarded child (Carr, J. 1974, Wolfensberger 1968). It is not a lesser form of casework and the counsellor is not necessarily less well trained than the caseworker for his particular task. Indeed, in the light of research findings (see below) a more focused approach might be likely to meet with more success. Only social workers describe what they do as casework but many professionals will have a counselling function, for example, lawyers, doctors, accountants.

Any definition of casework will invite numerous objections but for the purpose of this book, we define it as a method which aims through a professional relationship that is personal, reliable, accepting, and holding, and through particular skills and techniques, to help a client to use his own good judgment, social skills, problem-solving, and planning abilities to bring about some desired change within the client or his environment.

CASEWORK THEORY

In the past, casework has relied heavily on psychoanalytic theory (Goldstein 1975) but this is changing, and concepts drawn from anthropology, sociology, systems theory, communications theory, political theory, and from all schools of psychology, including learning theory, are regularly used. Our focus for understanding problems is the family and its environment and even when working with individuals we consider it important to do it within this framework. However, within this framework we are likely to use any concept (wherever it originates) which will increase understanding of ourselves and our clients. We favour a problem-focused approach to casework not only because it lends itself to clear definitions of goals and a clear focus for work, but also because it allows for a flexible use of techniques and interventions.

EVALUATION

The practice of casework has received a great deal of justified criticism. It has remained particularly vulnerable because its practitioners have made few adequate attempts to evaluate their work or to determine the relevance of casework to particular situations. Most studies that have been undertaken have shown casework to be ineffective (Goldberg 1973). As discussed in Chapter 1, attempts to evaluate therapy are bedevilled with difficulties. One study which did produce some positive and useful results was that of Reid and Shyne (1969) in which a comparison was made between short-term, focused casework and a long-term, open-ended approach. The short-term group made greater progress. Apart from the time limit, the content of the interviews in this group were characterized by less passive exploration and more working towards change. Mayer and Timms (1970) found that their sample of working-class clients was generally more satisfied with a directive approach. Additional evidence supporting a more focused approach comes from a study carried out by Gibbons and his colleagues (1979). They looked at casework done with clients who had been admitted to a casualty department after taking an overdose, and found that task-centred casework including agreement on target-problems, work on specific tasks, and adherence to a time limit, was more successful than routine after-care. Here, a focused approach was combined with intervention at the point of crisis (see Rapoport 1970).

Rose and Marshall's study (1974) of counselling in schools, provided some evidence of success in cutting down rates of delinquency. One way in which this study compared with other less successful studies, was that the counsellor had a full-time appointment and focused on problems as they were presented by the children (Goldberg 1973).

WHEN TO USE INDIVIDUAL CASEWORK WITH PARENTS

Wherever possible, the whole family should be included in any assessment of a presenting problem, and usually the whole family should be involved in any intervention. However, there are times when an individual approach with a parent, caretaker, or other significant adult is the most appropriate one to take. We consider the main indications to be:

(a) When there are practical limitations to family therapy, for example, the whole family refuses to be seen together, or the policy of a particular agency might make it very difficult to see families.

(b) When a child is receiving a special form of individual help, for example, psychotherapy (see below) or behaviour modification (see Chapter 8) and a parent may need help supporting a child through it.

(c) When a parent needs counselling in the handling of a particular problem, such as an autistic child (Howlin *et al.* 1973), a mentally retarded child (Wolfensberger 1968), a temperamentally difficult child (Thomas *et al.* 1968), or a child with physical illness (Magràb 1978).

Counselling may often not be child-focused, but more concerned with welfare rights and education, or methods of dealing with organizations. Many workers have built up a particular expertise in this area, but others know little. Social workers must be wary of giving unsatisfactory advice and if necessary be prepared to refer the client for expert advice.

(d) When a parent has difficulties of his or her own that do not substantially involve the family.

(e) When a family approach has failed or the family appears completely rigid and unchanging.

In most cases it would be most appropriate for both parents to be seen. If one parent is seen, it is only second best and may be due to reasons such as inappropriate time of appointment, or unsatisfactory attempts to engage a particular client.

STAGES OF THE CASEWORK PROCESS

(a) *Assessment* (see Chapter 3)

We consider that when possible there should be a family assessment, and only after this assessment has been made should decisions be taken concerning the most appropriate interventions. If casework is chosen as an intervention, it should be for definite and communicable reasons. In the past, there has been a tendency in the child guidance clinic for the social worker, as a matter of course, to see the parent(s) and for the psychiatrist, psychologist or psychotherapist to see the child. The length of casework has often been determined by the length of the child's therapy. Clearly, this is unsatisfactory. The social worker in the community has often worked with the mother (with or without the child present) because it is she who is at home during the day, appointments often being unplanned. It is essential to write in the file reasons for particular interventions being chosen.

(b) *Planning*

The next task is to formulate the aims for the casework intervention and from these the individual focuses for work. It is useful to set an initial time limit at the end of which the client and worker will decide whether or not to extend the period of work. This provides a discipline for both worker and client. Aims should be formulated in more general terms and include areas that may not be enlarged upon in the initial time period. The focuses should be narrow and concrete, preferably decided upon with the client and framed in such a way that progress can easily be reviewed.

Carol, aged 13, was referred to the clinic by her general practitioner. The referral was requested by mother at the recommendation of the school. At home Carol was described as rude, disobedient, and unhelpful. She frequently argued with mother and her mentally retarded elder brother, but more especially with Mr B., mother's cohabitee and future husband. It seemed to be the making of definite wedding plans that triggered-off the current intensity of difficulties and mother had, at the time of referral, decided to postpone the wedding. At school, Carol, an intelligent girl, was producing little work and proving a disruptive element in class. Two important facts emerged at assessment; firstly, that both Carol's mother and school were particularly strict and had rather unreal expectations of a young adolescent, and, secondly, that Mr B. had moved into the house four years previously while Carol's father was terminally ill. A family, as well as an individual assessment, was made, and as the clinic was not family-oriented pressures were exerted to take an individual approach. (Due to counter-pressure from the workers involved, this was changed to a family approach at a later date.) Carol was seen for 'supportive psychotherapy' and mother was taken on for casework. The main aims for casework were formulated thus: (1) To help mother to adjust her expectations of Carol. (2) To encourage the development of positive areas of their relationship. (3) To uncover the family secret surrounding father's death and Mr B.'s relationship with mother, on the assumption that unexpressed feelings about this were being acted-out by Carol. (4) To explore mother's feelings about re-marriage, on the basis that Carol's 'bad behaviour' was probably being used to delay this.

An initial time period of three months (twelve weekly meetings) was decided upon and after discussion with mother, three focuses were drawn up: (1) To clarify the nature of Carol's disobedience and to compare it to the sort of behaviour common in normal adolescence. (2) To explore the reasons for mother's difficult relationship with Carol when she did not find any apparent difficulty with her other four children. (3) To discuss ways of encouraging a positive relationship between mother and Carol. The reader will notice that no mention of the re-marriage was made at this point, as it was felt it would be unproductive, although it was retained as an overall aim.

(c) Engaging the client

Sometimes a successful working relationship is formed immediately and at other times it will take a period of time. If engagement is not achieved within the first few sessions, the focus for intervention (or even the intervention method) is probably wrong. One common obstacle is when the worker and client see the problem in a completely different way. For instance, Mrs T. saw her 6 year-old adopted daughter as thoroughly bad and a disruptive influence on the family, whilst the worker saw the child as a scapegoat within the family, and worked along these lines. No progress was made until the worker was able to accept the mother's feelings about the family and the fact that it did not meet her aspirations. A compromise focus was achieved from which further work could develop.

Occasionally, resistance is so strong that it is necessary to make a challenge, such as; 'I am not prepared to see the problem in the way you do at present and am sure that other problems exist. If you do not want to discuss them then that is your decision and you are free to seek help elsewhere.' Obviously, in situations where there are statutory obligations, for example, a child in care, it is not appropriate to send a client elsewhere, but such a challenge can be made without the withdrawal of help.

Another common obstacle is when the worker identifies with the child, and because of this is unable to form a helping relationship with the parent. Because childhood and its inevitable periods of stress is common to all of us, it is especially important in child-focused problems to be aware of the way in which our own feelings and experiences impinge on our professional relationships.

Parents almost inevitably bring a degree of guilt with them when they seek professional help, and this can stand in the way of progress. The worker must beware of reinforcing guilt and, when appropriate, acknowledge it. There is a difficult balance to be achieved between concentrating on the positive aspects of a mother's relationships with her family and being careful to acknowledge failure when a client presents it. It is not helpful to deny the severity of the problem. This will only lead the client to feel misunderstood.

CASEWORK STRATEGIES

This is by no means an exhaustive list. Workers are encouraged to use any strategy that seems potentially useful.

(a) Ventilation.   Allowing a client to unburden immediate feelings is often important, and useful, but should be used as a step in working towards change.

(b) Clarification.   It is often through discussion with the worker that a client is able to think more clearly about an action and to weigh-up the merits of different courses of action. Although the worker must avoid imposing her own views, it is often appropriate to be quite active – always bearing in mind not only the practical difficulties, but also the feelings which may limit particular actions.

(c) Encouragement.   Many clients will lack confidence in their parenting abilities, and many will fail to notice those things which they can do well. Acknowledgement of these can be very productive; encouragement to take new courses of action or to enter into negotiations, for instance, with solicitors or housing departments, may also be of great value.

(d) Limiting the focus of the interview.   At times it is inevitably necessary to draw back the discussion to the tasks in hand.

(e) Behaviour modification techniques.   These are discussed in detail in Chapter 8. The setting of tasks (for example, instructions to spend a certain length of time each day doing enjoyable things with a child) is a very useful strategy. Instructions on behaviour modification techniques that may be helpful in dealing with a child's difficulty can also be incorporated within a casework relationship.

(f) Promotion of insight. In our opinion, interpretations about the reasons for a client's behaviour should be linked to current events, understandable to the client, and useful in pursuing the task in hand. However brilliant an interpretation, if not understood by the client it is irrelevant. It should also be remembered that there is no evidence to show that insight, *per se*, promotes change.

(g) Termination. By working to a time limit, many of the problems associated with termination disappear. However, one still has to be aware that the client may have become rather dependent on the helping process and be experiencing feelings of rejection. This can be lessened by the worker remaining available for advice and future help. This can often be done by telephone. Termination is called for when the intervention has been successful, has failed, or some external factor, for example, a move to another house, has intervened.

Casework with children

In the child guidance clinic it is only recently that social workers have seen children individually. However, in the community, especially when involved with children who are in the care of the local authority or on supervision orders, the social worker has considerable direct contact with children. Such contact is often irregular and crisis-centred, but an ability to use this time to the full is very valuable.

(i) DEFINITION

We agree with Berry (1972) that casework with children is essentially no different from casework with adults although a child is, of course, less able to make decisions for himself. It may be more difficult for a child to cope with time limits as the whole concept of time is impossible for a young child to grasp. Although the caseworker should always have clearly defined aims, it is less easy with younger children to keep to particular focuses for work. Although the boundaries between casework and child psychotherapy are blurred, it is useful to make some distinctions. Winnicott (1968) says that the psychotherapist begins with the inner world of the child, whereas the caseworker's starting-point is the child functioning in the real world. This is the same sort of distinction that is made in work with adults.

(II) EVALUATION

There is no useful research evaluating casework with younger children. Rose and Marshall's study (1974) does indicate that counselling with children in secondary school can be effective in reducing delinquency.

(III) INDICATIONS FOR CASEWORK WITH CHILDREN

(1) When there are practical limitations to family therapy, casework may be chosen as an alternative to psychotherapy.
(2) When a family approach has failed.
(3) When a child is in the care of a local authority, and no family or substitute-family exists.

(IV) COMMUNICATING WITH THE CHILD

The reader will find it useful to read the section on psychotherapy and the relevant parts of Chapter 3 on assessment. Berry (1972) describes some of the difficulties that handicap a worker in communicating with a child. These include the child's limited vocabulary, limited ability to conceptualize (especially in terms of time and space), confusion between the real and the imaginary, and a grasshopper mind which does not keep to the point. If we watch and listen and provide a measure of security, children can communicate a great deal in a less cluttered and devious way than that used by an adult. Many children lack the experience of having an adult who listens to and talks to them. It may be necessary to make clear, in simple language, that this is what the caseworker is there for. The child may have many unspoken fears about a worker's power to take him away from home, or that she might disclose to his parents what he says. A child who has been abused by his parents may be unwilling to talk about his relationship with his parents because he fears that either he or his parents will be punished. .

Michael had been regularly abused by his mother, who, after a while, used the clinic for support through difficulties. It was decided that Michael, who thought he deserved the abuse, should be seen individually. It was only when the position of the worker *vis-à-vis* the mother was made clear to Michael that he realized that the worker really wanted to help his mother, and not find evidence to punish her or to remove Michael from home. From then on he was able to talk about what went on at home.

It has been customary for social workers to take the children under their supervision to the park or for a meal when they make their statutory visit. This outing is usually very welcome, but it could be that a quiet place with plenty of toys and a measure of time would be more helpful to the younger child to communicate with the worker.

Sarah had been taken into the care of the local authority for what was hoped to be a temporary period. The worker had been involved before the admission to care and continued to visit regularly while Sarah was in care. Sarah had a room of her own and the worker brought a set of toys each time she came, with which Sarah played whilst in her room with the worker. The dolls' house especially was an important mode of communication and Sarah acted out fears and hopes through the family of dolls. Frequently, the mother doll was killed by the daddy doll and Sarah was able to share her fears for her mother when she was not at home.

(v)   POSSIBLE DIFFICULTIES

The worker must always remember that the child's relationship with caretakers is in the long run more important than his relationship with the caseworker, who must be wary of competing for the child's affections. Further, the child's feelings (of anger or sadness) are sometimes so overwhelming to the worker that she finds it difficult to help the child cope with them.

Winnicott (1968) sums up the process of social casework with children as; (i) to reach the child and construct a working relationship, (ii) to look at the world with him and sort out his feelings, (iii) then to try and consolidate the positive things in the child himself and his world.

Individual psychotherapy

Although few social workers are trained psychotherapists, we have pointed out that there is a blurred distinction between casework and psychotherapy. It is important for social workers to consider the theory and techniques of psychotherapy, not only because it may prove useful in their own work but also because they may have clients for whom psychotherapy may be helpful and it is crucial to be aware of what that might entail.

DEFINITIONS

The term 'psychotherapy' in its broadest sense refers to the method of treating problems based on the use of psychological rather than physical techniques. Most commonly, the term is used to describe those treatments which involve talking. Psychotherapy may be practised in an individual, group, or family setting, and it may be 'supportive' or 'interpretive'. Psychoanalysis is a very specific form of psychotherapy which is dependent exclusively upon the use of interpretations to bring to consciousness the unconscious content of symptoms and behaviour (Smirnoff 1971). In this section, we concentrate on individual psychotherapy with children.

The essence of child psychotherapy is the use of the relationship between the therapist and the child to help resolve the child's problem. The medium for communication might be any combination of talking, drawing, and play. *Play therapy* utilizes toys, drawings and other play material to help the understanding and expression of unconscious and otherwise uncommunicated material. Winnicott (1971a) describes the use of a drawing game to facilitate therapeutic communication. In this, the therapist makes some kind of impulsive line drawing and invites the child to turn it into something. The child then makes a squiggle for the therapist to turn into something. The squiggles are used as the medium for communication.

The theories underlying the use of child psychotherapy are too complex to be discussed in detail here, and the interested reader is referred to Smirnoff's book *The Scope of Child Analysis* (1971) in which the various theories and therapies are outlined, compared, and contrasted. The majority of child psychotherapists and analysts in this country have been most influenced by Anna Freud, Melanie Klein, or Donald Winnicott.

THE THERAPY

The finer details of the therapy and the role of the therapist are determined by his or her personality and theoretical orientation. Most psychotherapists will have a standard set of play equipment and some arrange for each child to have his own set. Play material usually includes a sand-tray, a sink with available water, a dolls' house or equivalent, Play-people, modelling material, crayons, and paper. The therapist provides an age-appropriate explanation for their meeting, for example, 'I am seeing you to help you with your troubles. Some children who are upset or who have worries, find it helpful to talk and play, or draw a picture. We will be together in this room for a time each week and you may do any of these things.'

John, a 5 year-old boy, referred because of his failure to grow and refusal to eat, played a game with the Play-people in which the daddy-figure shouted at the mummy-figure and then went out to work. The mummy-figure then shouted at and smacked the baby-figure who pushes his dinner away. The therapist was able to make a direct link between John's distress at seeing his parents argue and his expression of that dismay by refusing to eat.

The therapist aims to be warm, friendly, sympathetic, and non-judgmental, but may also need to set limits on what the child may do in the interview, for instance, leaving the room or hitting the therapist. He has to strike a fine balance between facilitating self-expression and containing violent or destructive impulses. This can be particularly difficult when dealing with negative transference feelings.

The length and frequency of psychotherapy varies. A typical arrangement would be for therapy to occur at weekly intervals for 30–40 minutes. In child analysis, the sessions may be up to five times a week and continue for several years. The following example illustrates the sort of content of child psychotherapy.

Alice was referred for psychotherapy at the age of 7, two years after her parents had separated. Since the age of 3 she had been sullen, defiant, disobedient and destructive. After separation, the parents remained on reasonably amicable terms and her father visited the family at alternate weekends. The mother planned to re-marry. Alice was particularly aggressive towards both her father and future step-father (known to her as David).

Alice was seen at weekly intervals by a male therapist, to whom, initially, she related warmly. She involved him in play and clearly enjoyed the sessions. Her drawings and games emphasized her preoccupation with bad men. Alice repeatedly drew pictures of mountains which a group of mountaineers were struggling to conquer. The picture was always completed by the insertion of a little girl planting a flag at the top of the mountain. The therapist would comment on Alice's obvious enjoyment of the sessions and con-trasted this with her feelings about her father and David. The reaction to such comments was quite violent: she would tear up her drawings, throw the crayons across the room and try to leave. Later she became physically aggressive towards the therapist. He firmly contained her attacks and interpreted them as an expression of how she felt towards her father and David. He sympathized with her feel-ings and encouraged her to express verbally her resentment. Over a period of several months she became able to talk about her feelings of sadness and rejection. The difficult behaviour both at home and in therapy diminished, and after one year therapy ceased with minimal behaviour problems.

THE VALUE OF PSYCHOTHERAPY

Although the value of psychotherapy as an effective intervention has not been established (Winefield and Peay 1980: 145), it is widely used both by the trained and the untrained. It is certainly a useful means of gaining an insight into the child's inner world. There are no formal indications or contra-indications for its use. Clearly, when a child has no family or the family is unwilling to participate in therapy, an individual approach is necessary. However, it may be more appropriate to refer the child for casework or supportive psycho-therapy rather than interpretive psychotherapy or psychoanalysis. It might also be of use when the family approach fails or when the child has suffered gross deprivation.

The individual oriented therapist may strongly disagree, but we concur with Graham (1974) who has questioned the practice of child psychotherapy in the absence of any evidence for its usefulness.

Conclusions

Although individual casework, counselling, and psychotherapy are amongst the most commonly used techniques for helping the disturbed child and his family, there is little evidence for their overall value. However, there is some indication that a more focused approach achieves better results. As there are times when an individual approach is indicated, such as in situations of privation, deprivation, or non-co-operation, we consider clearly formulated aims and careful evaluation of progress to be essential.

7

Groupwork and group therapy

Introduction

Many workers involved in helping children and their families have used groupwork and group therapy as a technique. However, they have not always been successful and we suspect that lack of knowledge, preparation, and supervision combined with lack of experience are factors responsible for failure and disillusionment. Although there has been little evaluation of groupwork with children (Rutter 1975) there has been a good deal written and there is plenty to be learned both from the successful and unsuccessful experiences of others.

Some special characteristics of a group as a treatment medium are that it provides a wide range of relationships and more sources of feedback than one-to-one treatments (Rose 1975). Groups also provide the opportunity for members to help others rather than being cast only in the role of patient. As a result of this, it may be easier for clients who have difficulty with authority to function in a group (Thompson and Kahn 1970). There is no evidence to suggest that groups are an economical form of treatment and they demand a considerable input from the therapist. However, it has been suggested that seeing clients in groups for intake purposes might be a quicker way of seeing clients (Pincus and Minahan 1973).

Groupwork

Sturton (1972) distinguishes groupwork from group therapy by its criteria for intervention. The group therapist uses the individual's need for treatment or help as the criterion, whereas a group worker is concerned with helping small groups to carry out their tasks. As the task of some of these small groups may be to help individuals, it can be appreciated that there is no clear difference. The group worker, trained and experienced both in working with many different types of group and supervising others, would most likely act as a consultant, and we can see a strong argument for every agency having access to such a person as well as to someone who is experienced in analytic group techniques. Together with the setting up and running of 'treatment' groups, Sturton points out other areas where groupwork can be of use and these are certainly relevant to work with children. One of these is with other groups, for example, social clubs and playgroups; another is with ill-supported people in the front-line of service, for example, child-minders and home tutors; and also for clients (here we also include staff) in group-living conditions, for example community home or homeless family accommodation. Indeed, in utilizing the potential of existing groups or individuals through the medium of a group, one might help to prevent future problems. For instance, a child-minder receiving support through a group of other child-minders might well be able to survive difficulties with a child, and so the placement may be saved from breaking down with the consequent disruption for the child and his family.

Group therapy

In group therapy as in individual therapy, the content will vary considerably according to the training and inclinations of the therapist.

(1) GROUP PLAY THERAPY

This is a form of group therapy for children aged 3–13. Ginott (1971) suggests that for a child to gain any help from a group he needs to have 'social hunger' or a desire to socialize. Other therapists agree that children who have lacked an early, satisfactory one-to-one relationship and so have not progressed to develop this 'social hunger' cannot cope with a group situation (Gorell Barnes 1975a, Joselyn 1972). There is general agreement that a group should contain no more than five children. The problems the children are experiencing should be different, so that they are more able to share. Five children all suffering gross deprivation are unlikely to benefit from a group experience.

It is, of course, important to have a suitable setting in which the group can take place. The ideal room is neither too large so that children run around wildly, nor so small that everyone gets in each other's way. In a group that we ran, the room had a large cupboard into which, every so often, the children would crawl. This provided both a place which felt safe enough to share confidences and a retreat when a group member was feeling sad or angry. There should be a good variety of toys, including a doll's house, dolls, puppets, toy animals, and opportunities for drawing, playing with clay, and painting. Older children will need construction toys, games, sewing, a typewriter, as well as younger age-group toys. We found cooking a particularly useful activity which readily seemed to bring the conflicts and worries of home into the group room.

Although aiming for an enabling and permissive atmosphere in the group room, it is necessary to set some limits on the children's behaviour. In our experience, it is necessary to do this from the beginning or one may end up with chaos – frightening for everyone. A ban on physical violence and deliberate breaking of toys is necessary but there should be no limits set for symbolic play. If a child does break the limits set, the therapist should aim to deal with it within the session although it may be necessary to place the child outside the group-room for a short time. We found that physically holding an angry or sad child was useful and would help the child feel accepted by us.

In this kind of group there is no problem with silence. There is a wealth of material and the difficulty is what to do with that material. The psychoanalytic approach involves trying to translate action into words, and Ginott (1971) points out that eventually the children will make verbal interpretations to each other. Interpretations should, of course, be understandable to all group members. Slavson (1955) advocates a more passive role for the therapist and sees the 'activity' of the group members as the main form of communication.

The aims of group play therapy are more likely to be couched in terms of personality-change rather than simple symptom-improvement and the goals formulated for each individual in the group rather than group goals being set (Rose 1975). Transference can be very intense, and it is important to be aware of this. In a group that we ran together when the male therapist was absent for one week, although the children had been prepared, they all reacted with great anger. We had failed to realize that as several of the children had no father at home, it would bring to the group all the emotion belonging to their father's death or departure.

There has been little satisfactory evaluation of group play therapy and as Frank and Zilbach (1968) point out, this type of therapy will benefit only a small number of children. Because of the great investment of time, resources and facilities needed to run such a group, it will not be a viable form of help for all agencies to offer. However, it can be useful and is interesting and informative, and it is only through the running and assessment of groups that any necessary modifications to this form of help can be made.

(II) BEHAVIOUR THERAPY GROUPS

An individual is referred to this kind of group with the goal of improving a particular difficulty that he experiences (for example, lack of social skills, aggressive behaviour). Thus goals are framed individually, but it is through *group tasks* (see below) that these are achieved. Rose (1975) suggests that the therapist attempts to replicate as nearly as possible the situation in which the problem behaviour occurs. Thus, it would be helpful to hold groups for children who are aggressive in the classroom on school premises. He also emphasizes the need to make the group as attractive as possible because a child has to attend in order to benefit from the group. Children may be grouped because of diverse symptoms or grouped with the same problem, although there must be a variety in the intensity of the problem so that group members can actively help one another.

The following is an outline of some of the strategies (including group tasks) used in behaviour therapy groups:

Use of reinforcements (see also pp. 141–42). These can be social reinforcements such as praise or a cuddle, or tangible reinforcements such as toys or sweets.

Role-playing or behavioural rehearsal.   Lazarus (1966) found that role-playing was more effective than non-directive therapy or advice in effecting behavioural change. In this strategy, the therapist isolates a particular behaviour which needs improvement, for example, an interview with the headmistress, or going into a shop to purchase something. The situation is then set up with staff or group members playing the different roles. The behaviour should be in the repertoire of most of the members of the group so that they can contribute to the criticism and advice. This strategy can be particularly helpful in social skills training (Pease 1979).

Games and activities as group tasks.   The therapist chooses tasks which provide the child with practice in behaviour that usually holds difficulties. Outings are useful for a child who lacks confidence in public, whilst co-operative games are helpful for children who find it difficult to share. Again, the task should be within the ability of most members of the group.

Training.   Some knowledge and experience of both behaviour and group therapy is necessary to run this type of group. It is possible for inexperienced therapists to join a group in an auxiliary role and so receive close supervision.

(III) TALKING GROUPS

Groups for adolescents.   Although this book does not strictly include the adolescent age-group, talking groups may also be used for pre-adolescent children. A group can be a useful medium for an adolescent to examine his own feelings, actions, and experiences, and hopefully to gain new insights from other group members who may help and support him in changes he decides to make in his behaviour. It also provides an opportunity for gaining first-hand experience of his impact on others. We recommend Berkowitz's book *Adolescents Grow in Groups* (1972) for those working with an older age-group. The ideal number for this group is generally considered to be 6–8 older adolescents or 5–6 younger children and there should be little age-spread. Berkowitz suggests that a mixed sex group has great advantages, whereas Anthony (1965) says that this is too disturbing for most adolescents. It seems best to have either male and female co-therapists or a therapist of the same sex as the majority of group members.

Material will not flow so freely as with very young children, and interpretations should be kept to material that is immediate and thus available to all group members (Gorell Barnes 1975a). It may be useful to include some members who have experience of being in a group. The rules and limits of the group should be decided before-hand and outlined at the first group.

There have been various attempts to evaluate groups for ado-lescents and some success has been reported, especially with institutionalized adolescents (Robins 1973).

Parents' groups. Groups have been run for parents, mothers, mothers and children, and whole families (Leichter and Schulman 1974) as a main form of help or in addition to other help, such as residential care or psychotherapy. In some groups, all the members share similar problems, whilst in other groups their problems are dis-similar. Ginott (1971) outlines three levels of therapy for parents' groups – group psychotherapy (in which the aims involve personality change), group counselling (in which the aims involve parents under-standing their difficulties in relation to their children and other family members and providing ventilation of feelings) and, lastly, group guidance (aiming to improve the every-day functioning of parents). Gorell Barnes (1975a) has described the use of groups in a school setting for the parents of disadvantaged children.

Some areas of difficulty

Obtaining referrals. It may be necessary to indulge in a good deal of public relations work in order to obtain suitable referrals, either because other professionals may be dubious about the group, or because there may be a tendency for them to refer only their failures (Sturton 1972).

Liaison. Rose (1975) points out that the therapeutically constituted group is only one of the many groups to which a child belongs, and for the child to have support both in attending the group and using what he has learned in life outside, it is necessary to have the co-operation of other professionals (Hickin 1971, Sturton 1972) and, of course, parents (Gorell Barnes 1975b).

Co-therapy. Co-therapy is often used in an attempt to share the burden of a group, but anyone who has had experience of it will know that it presents its own difficulties. Co-therapists must be able to plan and work together. Waterhouse (1978) describes attempts to set up group work in an intermediate treatment project, and it would appear that the inability to come to agreements about rules and strategy jeopardized the success of the project. Particular problems may arise when therapists from different professions join together to run a group (Nurse 1972).

Conclusions

Group work and group therapy have an important contribution to make in child-focused problems. Traditional group therapy with children has limitations but behaviour oriented groups, group therapy with parents, and work with various groups within the community may prove valuable. There is a need for more satisfactory evaluation of this range of techniques.

8
Behaviour modification

Introduction

Many social workers bristle at the mere mention of 'behaviour modification'. Nevertheless, it would be difficult to argue that social workers are not in the business of changing behaviour or 'behaviour modification', however strongly we cling to concepts such as 'self-determination' or 'non-directiveness'. Indeed, these concepts have been radically re-examined in the light of a growing number of different schools and methods of social work (Rapoport 1970, Pincus and Minahan 1973). Inevitably, as social workers involve themselves with families, groups, and communities, it becomes obvious that one person's freedom may take away the freedom from someone else. It would seem that even the most passive psychotherapist cannot escape from being a 'shaper of behaviour'. Truax examined eighty-five non-directive interviews conducted by Carl Rogers. He found that the therapist, despite a total commitment to therapist neutrality, differentially rewarded and increased the frequency of certain client behaviours through the selective application of empathy, acceptance, and directiveness (Truax 1966). Indeed, following on from this, it has been argued that if this 'learning component is inevitably a part of psychotherapy, then a more deliberate application of the knowledge of learning theory might make psychotherapy more effective' (Stuart 1967: 219).

When a client arrives at a social work agency it is usually with a complaint about his or someone else's behaviour and goals, for help will almost inevitably be couched in terms of changing someone's behaviour. This is perhaps even more true when the client is a child or a family. We think, therefore, that an understanding of learning theory and behaviour modification techniques could be one possible contribution towards the success of some of these aims, especially as there is a good deal of evidence to suggest that these kinds of techniques (Kolvin *et al.* 1972, Marks 1974, Kennedy 1971) are particularly helpful with certain problems. We do not, however, urge all social workers to become competent clinical psychologists but only that some of these techniques should be included in the social worker's repertoire. We think also that there are particular skills, for example, recording, defining and planning of goals, monitoring feedback, which have been developed more highly in psychology than in social work and it would be foolish not to take account of these.

In this section we firstly outline some of the theories underlying behaviour modification techniques; secondly, comment on some of the main problem areas in children for which this technique has proved effective, and, thirdly, draw together some of the main considerations in formulating a behaviour modification programme.

Learning theory

We do not intend to discuss the theories underlying behaviour modification in any great detail, partly because there has been a great deal written on the subject already, and partly because it would be a task too great for this book. However, we think it would be helpful to remind readers of some of the basic theories.

Some general characteristics of learning theory

(1) The most basic assumption is that all behaviour is learned and that different learning theories are concerned with *how* behaviour is learned and maintained.
(2) Learning theory presupposes a mechanistic rather than an organismic model of Man. In other words, it sees Man as someone who reacts to his environment rather than being the source of acts, and believes that even complex behaviours can be reduced to a chain-reaction of stimulus events leading to responses which then become stimuli in their own right, and so on (Bandura 1974).

(3) Although biological factors are not denied by learning theorists (especially by Eysenck 1967, Bandura 1969, and Ross 1972) they have on the whole been given minimal attention.

(4) The basic learning theory approach to therapy is that it should consist of unlearning, re-learning, or new learning, and not of tackling any underlying cause. This does not, however, mean that all theorists believe that by removing the symptom the whole disorder has been removed also.

(i) CLASSICAL CONDITIONING (sometimes called respondent learning)

This is the form of learning illustrated by Pavlov. The essential operation is the pairing of two stimuli – one initially neutral (the conditioned stimulus) and the other, one that consistently elicits a response (the unconditioned stimulus). As a result of the pairing of the two stimuli they come to elicit the same response. A parent will usually say 'No' to a baby when removing him from a problem situation. Eventually the child will learn to respond to the word 'No' alone.

Other aspects of classical conditioning are: extinction of response, spontaneous recovery of conditioned response, and stimulus generalization. If the conditioned stimulus is continually presented on its own without the unconditioned stimulus, eventually the response will not occur. However, a conditioned response that .has been extinguished may spontaneously recover some of the strength lost in extinction, thus showing that the association between the two stimuli can exist even after extinction. Another important phenomenon is that of stimulus generalization. Pavlov found that when he conditioned his dogs to salivate to the sound of a bell, they did so in response to the sound of a buzzer as well.

As Jehu et al. (1972) point out, classical conditioning is especially important in the acquisition of problematic emotional responses such as anxiety and fear and he quotes the classic experiment by Watson and Rayner (1920) with an 11 month-old child called Albert. Albert was afraid (unconditioned responses) of loud noises (unconditioned stimulus). He was presented with a white rat while a loud noise was sounded behind his head. After a number of pairings, presentation of the rat alone (conditioned stimulus) produced a fear response (now the conditioned response). Similar stimuli such as rabbits, and human hair, also evoked a fear response (stimulus generalization). If we can for a moment disregard the rather dubious ethics of this particular experiment, it does serve to illustrate how some fears may be learned. Indeed, there is a great deal of clinical evidence to show how phobias have emerged in this way (for example, Freeman and Kendrick 1964, Lazarus 1960, Lazarus, Davison and Polefka 1965, Kushner 1965). However, not all psychologists would accept a simplistic model of the acquisition of fear and many would agree that there are probably many other contributory factors involved, especially in the less specific phobias such as agoraphobia (Marks 1969).

(II) INSTRUMENTAL LEARNING OR OPERANT LEARNING

Perhaps a simple way of describing this process of learning is to state that a response which produces a reward will become stronger whilst one which does not produce a reward will become weaker. Most readers will know about B. F. Skinner and his rats; some were placed in a specially designed box which had in it a lever which when pressed produced a pellet of food. The rats pressed this by accident as part of their exploration of the box but soon learned that the pellet of food was produced following the pressing of the lever. This latter behaviour increased dramatically.

There is considerable evidence to show that operant learning accounts for a great deal of behaviour. Children soon learn to do things which gain rewards and it is not, of course, always only socially acceptable behaviour that receives rewards. McAuley and McAuley (1977) quote a case in which a 3 year-old child recently returned from hospital after a short stay, was displaying frequent tantrums and demanding to be carried. A psychologist went to the home to observe what was happening and found that the child's tantrums were frequently rewarded by getting what she wanted, while ordinary interaction was punctuated by frequent reprimands by mother. The child was displaying rewarded behaviour.

There are various aspects of operant learning about which it is useful to know. *Shaping of behaviour* is a process in which a reward is given when the subject approximates to a goal behaviour. Then the subject has to approximate the behaviour more closely before the reward is given, until eventually only the goal behaviour itself elicits a reward.

An understanding of how behaviour can be shaped is of great importance therapeutically. Shaping is a technique often used in dealing with problem behaviour in children, and with some speech difficulties. One application of this is that the child is at first rewarded for any vocalization, and then for an approximation to the word required, and finally only for vocalizing the correct word.

The concepts of *primary and secondary reinforcement* are often encountered. Quite simply, primary reinforcements are those which reduce some innate physiological need, for example, hunger, and secondary reinforcements are those which after being paired with a primary reinforcer have now become reinforcers in their own right – praise and encouragement would be included in this group.

Because the use of reward training is central to a great deal of behaviour modification, we think it would be useful to mention *partial reinforcement*. When a behaviour is only partially reinforced some correct responses are rewarded and others are left unrewarded. This is usually administered to some plan or *schedule of reinforcement*, for example, every third response is rewarded. On the whole, learning is slower with partial reinforcement, but behaviour is maintained longer when reinforcement ceases.

(III) IMITATIVE BEHAVIOUR

This is a development from the above two forms of learning in that it presupposes a central organism that processes information rather than relying on a stimulus-response model. Bandura (1969) describes this type of learning most clearly. Imitative or observational learning, or modelling, is a process whereby a person observes someone else behaving and receiving the consequences of this behaviour. Bandura and Walters (1963) exposed nursery school children to real or filmed models of adults who exhibited unusual forms of aggression towards a large rubber doll. After only mild frustration this group of children imitated the models' behaviour and were more aggressive than similarly frustrated children who had not previously observed an aggressive model. One can postulate how, on this basis, children might learn a great deal from adults' behaviour, especially from adults they respect.

Most of the concepts discussed here are of use in understanding the behaviour modification techniques enlarged upon in the following section.

Conditions commonly treated with behaviour modification techniques

ENURESIS

One commonly used treatment is the bell and pad. This is a simple piece of apparatus which works to wake the child as soon as he urinates. The child sleeps on a special mat placed under his sheet. The pad is wired to a battery so that as soon as the sheet becomes wet and the electrical circuit is completed, a loud alarm sounds, and, hopefully, wakes the child. The process can best be understood in terms of classical conditioning, i.e., the contraction of the bladder prior to urinating is paired with the unconditioned stimulus of a bell sounding and thus becomes the conditioned stimulus provoking the conditioned response of waking. There do, however, seem to be other processes involved, for example, avoidance learning (Crosby 1950), and the gadget effect (De Leon and Mandell 1966), while Turner (1973) has pointed out that the use of a bell and pad may just be drawing the family's attention to the problem and dry nights are therefore more likely to be praised. Obviously, the way in which the bell and pad work is a good deal more complex than is at first apparent but it is by far the most effective remedy for this problem. In fact, three-quarters of children stop wetting after two or three months. One-third relapse after treatment, but most of these respond to a second course of treatment.

The social worker's role

The application of the bell and pad would normally be carried out by a doctor or a psychologist, although it has been used successfully by social workers (Morgan and Young 1972), but it might well be the social worker, through an understanding of the child's need and of treatment availability, who effects the referral and prepares the family. The success of treatment depends on a high level of parental co-operation in such matters as making sure that the child wakes when the bell rings, checking that the switch remains on, and being on hand to change sheets when they have become wet. Another necessity for success is suitable environmental conditions such as separate bed for the child and proximity to the parents so that they can hear the alarm. We know of one case where the bell and pad were ineffective because in wet weather the roof leaked on to the child's bed and set off the alarm! Obviously, the social worker involved with the family has an important role in encouraging and enabling the optimum conditions both through preparation and support of the whole family, and possibly also in providing practical help such as extra beds and bedding.

Bell and pad treatment is available through local child guidance clinics, child psychiatric departments, and special clinics run by area health authorities or the local education department, and in the case of Kent County Council by the social services department.

Star charts and reward systems

Another much simpler method used in helping enuretic and encopretic children (pp. 74–6) is the use of praise together with a star chart, sometimes coupled with the giving of a reward after the collection of à certain number of stars. In cases of enuresis, because this is a very simple method, it should always be used in the first instance and there is no reason why a social worker cannot advise on this form of help without the back-up help of psychiatrist or psychologist. Basically, the child is praised and encouraged for every dry night achieved. Together with the praise a star is awarded. The family is advised to make no fuss when the child wets the bed so that no reward of attention is given to reinforce the bed-wetting. In the case of encopresis it is advisable to obtain a medical opinion to ascertain whether the child is suffering an overflow of faeces due to chronic constipation, or is just depositing his faeces in the wrong place. The reasons for the former might be many and one common cause is that of toilet phobia (see p. 77). A star chart could be used to provide reward for the child as he makes steps towards using the toilet. A star chart might well be helpful if the child is just refusing to deposit his faeces where everyone else expects him to.

Roy was a boy of 8 who was referred for soiling his pants two or three times a day. He was the youngest of four children and came from a busy family in which there was little time to devote to him. In fact, it was obvious, observing the situation from the outside, that the time Roy received the most attention, albeit negative, was when he soiled. A reward system was set up by the therapist, in which Roy was awarded a star for every half-day he remained clean. After receiving four stars these were converted into a material reward that was agreed between Roy and his parents. The parents were also instructed not to make any fuss when Roy soiled himself. The results of therapy were good and Roy soon stopped soiling.

FEARS AND PHOBIAS (see pp. 55–6)

Behaviour modification appears to be an effective treatment for fears and phobias, especially of specific phobias. In studies with adults, it has been shown that behaviour therapy is more effective than psychotherapy (Marks 1974). Although there have been no large studies on phobias in children, there is no reason to believe that results would be different. Two behavioural techniques which may be useful in dealing with such problems are desensitization and modelling.

Desensitization

This is a process through which a child (or adult) 'unlearns' a fear or phobia. It is firstly very important to ascertain the exact circumstances in which the child shows fear. It is insufficient to rely on accounts of the fear given by others; the child should be observed in the phobic situation. For example, a child may be afraid of the dark, but are all 'dark' situations equally feared; alone or accompanied, outside or inside, familiar places or unfamiliar? It is also necessary to ascertain the intensity of fear experienced in these different situations. A 'hierarchy' is then drawn up in which a slightly-feared situation is first on the list, and the most-feared situation the last. Desensitization involves the client approaching the feared situation whilst feeling relaxed. Obviously, the first item in the hierarchy is attempted first, and so on, until the goal is attained. As fear and relaxation cannot exist at the same time, it is said that the relaxation 'inhibits the fear response'. Adult clients are often asked to 'imagine' feared situations, although with children it is better if the situation is 'real'. With children, relaxation can be achieved by introducing an enjoyable activity, for example, talking with an adult, listening to a favourite story, eating enjoyable food. It is important to maintain a state of relaxation and not to move to a higher item in the hierarchy until the previous one has been mastered.

Michael was a 4 year-old boy who soiled everywhere and appeared to be both phobic of the lavatory and of the potty. A hierarchy was drawn up, the first item being to sit on the potty in the living-room while reading a story with mother. Eventually the child defaecated in the potty. The potty was then moved in small distances until it was in the toilet and then a transfer was made so that the child used the toilet. At all stages the mother read to the child to create a state of relaxation rather than fear. As soon as Michael had reached the point of using the toilet he was able to use any toilet and did not need his mother to read to him, a common outcome to such treatment.

Some reports of the success of desensitization as a treatment are fear of cars (Lazarus 1960), buses and dogs (Obler and Terwilliger 1970), exam fears (Kondas 1967), and fear of the dark (Lazarus and Abramovitz 1962). Similar techniques have also been used for separation anxiety (Montenegro 1968).

If a child has a very entrenched phobia, a social worker with little experience of this technique should refer the child to a child psychiatric agency for assessment with a view to someone with more experience carrying out the treatment on his own or jointly with the social worker. However, a social worker could use a knowledge of this technique, for instance, to help a mother cope with many of the fears of childhood, for example, of animals, water, or the dark.

Flooding, or implosion, is a process whereby a client is brought into contact with the most-feared situation straightaway and kept in contact until fear disappears, on the basis that the anxiety reaches a peak and then diminishes, so allowing the client to experience the feared situation in the absence of anxiety. This is an effective technique in both children and adults (Rutter 1975) when correctly used, but should be left to the skilled practitioner.

SCHOOL PHOBIA

School phobia (or school-refusal) is a specific form of anxiety (p. 56) not to be confused with truanting (p. 56). The reasons for the phobia must be assessed; the fear may be based on real situations which could be altered, for example, fear of bullying, or of punishment for not having correct uniform, and there may also be many anxieties within the family. All of these issues need to be tackled, but most therapists (of any kind) also advocate an immediate return to school, if necessary accompanied by parent, social worker, or other helping person.

In behavioural terms, this would be the equivalent of 'flooding'. Others prefer a graded approach more akin to desensitization. Ross (1972) points out that the complex behaviours shown in school-refusal include attempts to avoid the fear situation, and that this avoidance response, because it reduces the fear, is itself reinforced. This response is often further reinforced by situations in the home. The normal child may well experience separation anxieties and also anxieties related to school, but usually the school situation provides enough reinforcement to overcome the anxieties. Kennedy (1971), following his study of fifty school phobics, advocates a rapid return to school and a good deal of help for parents, teachers, and children. The behaviour modification approach with its stress on the relief of the presenting symptom has perhaps minimized too much the part that family interaction plays, but it appears to provide a useful tool to cope with a very difficult problem. We must also stress the importance of the co-operation of other professionals who have connections with the child's schooling.

Trudie was 13 at the time of referral. She had never really settled into secondary school and attendance had always been poor, usually covered by a note from mother saying that she was ill. For the past year, Trudi had not attended at all. She had many worries concerning both school and separation from mother. The whole family was socially phobic, and there were many fears that they all shared concerning the world outside the family. The eldest girl, aged 16, had, after a shaky beginning, integrated into school, probably because she was bright, attractive, and good at sports. The youngest child, aged 10, showed signs of becoming phobic. We made an early return to school a priority and did this on a graded basis because of Trudi's many fears. A conference was held with the headmistress, housemistress, educational welfare officer, and educational psychologist, and the staff of the child guidance clinic, who were involved in the case. The educational welfare officer was given the responsibility for taking Trudi to school, first to the school gate, then into the school building, and so on, until eventually she could go unaccompanied to school, where she made friends with the help of her elder sister. This was a successful graded return to school. However, the family were also seen together and helped to deal with some of their anxieties, so that some of Trudi's concerns about her family were alleviated. Behaviour modification is often used in combination with other methods of help. Of course, the return of a phobic child to school is by no means always as straightforward as this, but in many cases it can be successfully achieved although requiring a great deal of concentrated work by everyone connected with the child.

ANTI-SOCIAL AND BEHAVIOUR PROBLEMS (see pp. 63–7)

This is another area where behaviour modification techniques, mainly based on operant conditioning and imitative learning, are well-established. Indeed, in the past decade these kinds of techniques have been highly developed. A social worker is often presented with complaints about a child's behaviour by a parent, school, or residential worker. It is useful, therefore, to have a working knowledge of some techniques which may be of help. As mentioned previously, the basis of operant conditioning is the modification of behaviour by reinforcements or reward. In analysing a situation where a child is reported to be behaving problematically, it is usually possible to see what the child gains from behaving the way he does. Also, it is often obvious what little reward he gets for behaving well. Another aspect of the situation worth noting is the way in which the child shapes the behaviour of the parent.

David, aged 4, created so much mayhem when disciplined in any way that both parents eventually gave up all attempts to do so, and David ruled the house, physically abusing his parents and breaking most of the furniture. The parents had always had problems in the area of discipline, but David had aimed at a weakness and seemingly had won.

Eysenck and Rachman (1965) point out that treatment in adults is mainly concerned with breaking down behaviour, but that in children new behaviour patterns often have to be built up, so that the therapist is concerned with both tasks.

Kevin, aged 7, was the middle child of three. Mother was in the process of being divorced after a stormy and violent marriage. Father's whereabouts were not known. Over the past few months, mother had developed a potentially permanent relationship. This prompted her to seek help with Kevin who was very difficult both at home and at school, having frequent violent tantrums, refusing to obey any instructions from mother, interfering with his siblings, and stealing. His behaviour at school mirrored that exhibited at home. Mother also complained that she shared nothing good with Kevin. Whatever the reasons for the genesis of Kevin's behaviour, at the time of referral it was obvious that Kevin was receiving no encouragement for whatever small amount of 'good' behaviour he exhibited. He was also getting a good deal of attention for his difficult behaviour. This reinforcement was not only from mother giving attention because she was made upset and angry, but also from the siblings, who rather enjoyed the excitement of Kevin's outbursts.

The use of parents, school and other agencies as behaviour modification co-therapists has been advocated by many, and this was the system used in this case. There is now quite a collection of manuals designed to be read by parents, etc., who are to be involved as therapists. We recommend especially *Families: Application of Social Learning to Family Life*, by Gerald R. Patterson (1971). Indeed, this would also make very good reading for any social worker embarking on this sort of help for the first time. It seems important that parents are well versed in the basic principles of social learning theory, although there is little evidence to show how this is best done. Kevin's mother read the manual and it was discussed with her. Inevitably this gives rise to considerable guilt as parents are faced with the fact that their child is responding to their own behaviour, and so it is very important to put this into perspective, pointing out that there is no perfect parent. It is also worth emphasizing that all children are different and that what works for one child (perhaps an elder sibling) does not necessarily work for another. A programme was constructed in which Kevin gained stars for certain defined co-operative behaviours, for example, going to bed when asked. Negative and aggressive behaviour was to be ignored as far as was possible. Of course, this can be difficult in a third-floor flat if the behaviour is noisy, but luckily, in this case, the co-operation of the family in the flat below was ensured. The two siblings were included in the discussion. Mother was also instructed to spend twenty minutes each day sharing an activity alone with Kevin. This led to mother discovering 'good' qualities in Kevin that she had forgotten existed. A psychologist simultaneously carried out a similar system with Kevin's class teacher, providing stars for good behaviour, and using 'time out', when Kevin's behaviour became impossible. 'Time out' is a technique in which a child showing uncontrolled behaviour is put for a short but agreed time in a non-reinforcing environment. In the home, this could be a room with no toys – a bathroom perhaps. The school used the corridor outside the classroom. Although there were setbacks, there was a considerable overall improvement in both areas of Kevin's behaviour and a good deal more positive responses from the adults surrounding him. If the reader, working in a setting which did not include psychologists, felt it useful to use teachers or school staff as co-therapists in this way, it may be worth trying to involve the help of local clinical or educational psychologists. We make this point because from experience we know the levels of resentment that can be built up if a relatively unknown social worker enters a school to add more work to an overworked teacher's load. One of the answers is for social work departments to build up mutually useful and supportive relationships with schools instead of contact usually arising from crisis. (See Chapter 9.)

Anti-social behaviour appears on the whole to be extremely difficult to treat (Rutter 1975). Amongst the more carefully conducted studies, Patterson and his colleagues (1973b) have evaluated the effectiveness of home-based behaviour modification techniques. After eight weeks of treatment there was a 60 per cent reduction in the occurrence of target behaviours.

The residential behaviour modification run at Achievement Place in Kansas has become quite well known. This is a small group home for delinquent boys, aged 12–16. The couple who run the home are trained in behavioural techniques and they use a sophisticated token economy system. Educational and social skills needs are met as far as possible. The boys gain academically, and after the first 6 years of the project are more likely to do well than if helped by traditional means (Fixson, Phillips and Wolf 1973).

NON-ACCIDENTAL INJURY

We discuss non-accidental injury in more detail in Chapter 4. Little has been written on the application of behavioural techniques to families where there has been violence towards, or negligence of, one or more children. However, Sutton (1979) describes a case in which a mother is given graded tasks designed to encourage positive contact with the injured child. This certainly seems to be a possible way of alleviating some situations. After crying, enuresis and encopresis have been found to be the next most common precipitants of non-accidental injury to children (Kempe and Helfer 1968) and so the use of behaviour methods could be tried with good effect. However, the possibility of failure may aggravate the situation, especially if a previous child has been treated successfully in this way (Morgan and Young 1972).

PROBLEMS OF ADOLESCENCE

Most behavioural techniques are of value in helping any age group, including adolescents. One technique of particular value in working with adolescents is the use of contracts. So often the crux of adolescent referrals is that the parents want a daughter or son who is different from their own, and neither does the adolescent think very much of his or her parents. Often, the making of a contract in which each 'side' offers defined concessions can be the beginning of a settlement. However, many families have no methods of negotiation and may need considerable help in drawing up a contract. Each aspect must be agreed upon by all parties, and then written down so that no misunderstanding, either real or contrived, can be made. The making of a contract seems to have met with some success both in the home and in school (Tharp and Wetzel 1969, Hamme et al. 1970).

Some general pointers when drawing up a behavioural programme

(a) McAuley and McAuley (1977) give six variables affecting the level of success in an individual case,

(i)   The type of problem and the number of different problems
(ii) The duration of a problem
(iii) Family pathology and motivation
(iv) The amount and intensity of therapy that can be made available
      – the value of long-term therapy seems to be in doubt
(v)   The effect of previously unsuccessful therapeutic approaches
(vi) The effectiveness of the therapist

The amount of work that needs to be put into this sort of therapy is, in the short-term, immense and it is important to choose cases which show some hope of success, for example, well-motivated clients with problems that are either simple or with which other therapists have had success.

(b) Information gathering: it is very important that information is very accurate. The therapist needs to know *what* the problem behaviour is, *how often* it occurs, the *intensity* of the behaviour, the *situation* in which it happens, and *precipitating* events. In gauging the resources of the family to take part in a programme, the therapist must ascertain other areas of difficulty, the basic skills and capabilities of the child and his family, and the usual methods of reward and punishment.

The therapist must assume that parental or child accounts of behaviour may not be accurate, for various reasons, and should observe the behaviour himself. Some level of training for observation seems helpful, and certainly we would advise some practice.

(c) The accurate recording of problem behaviours is important to obtain a 'baseline' from which to judge any improvement or deterioration during therapy. A chart should be drawn up in which the number of problem behaviours within a particular time period can be recorded. It is very important to be able to monitor progress during therapy, as quick feedback is an essential aspect of this kind of therapy.

Conclusions

Behaviour therapy is one of the few management techniques that have been shown to be effective. Its success depends on the careful employment of a variety of factors, all of which might usefully be applied to other therapies as well. Particular emphasis is placed on (i) the ability to focus on particular problems rather than a whole spectrum at once, (ii) the direct involvement of clients in the planning of treatment and the general openness of the approach, (iii) the use of parents and others as therapists with the possible economies this may eventually incur in that 'treatment' can continue after the social worker ceases involvement, (iv) careful and precise gathering and recording of information, (v) close monitoring of success of therapy, (vi) feedback to clients, and (vii) general scientific approach to treatment and its evaluation.

As with all therapeutic techniques, it is important to discuss the work with other colleagues to gain opinions, advice, and general feedback, and it may be possible if behaviour modification is a new venture, to persuade a local psychologist to supervise its use in the agency. Unlike most other therapeutic techniques, behaviour therapy has been shown to be effective. Because of this, we firmly advocate its use – it often involves a large input of work, but so does casework, for example, the success of which seems much less certain.

9
Consultation and liaison

Introduction

In this chapter we are concerned with direct contacts between professionals rather than between professional and client. Social work education has, in general, neglected this very important part of the social workers' task. Lack of skills in communicating with and using the expertise of colleagues undoubtedly leads to a poorer service for the client and an uneconomic use of resources. We focus on two main areas of communication: liaison and consultancy.

For our purposes 'liaison' refers to communications between professionals involved with the same client, client group, or project, to further their joint aims. At a time when there is little hope of services expanding, it is even more necessary for the service offered to operate as efficiently as possible. In child-focused problems, it is very common for a whole host of professionals (including perhaps the general practitioner, health visitor, teacher, local authority social worker, psychiatrist, and school counsellor) to be involved, and unfortunately, often each pursues his own course of action, with little common purpose. Clearly, this leads both to inefficiency on the part of the professional and confusion for the client. The answer is rarely for one worker to take on the whole task of helping the family, for it is unlikely that one person could carry all the knowledge and skills required. What is required is better liaison between all those concerned.

In addition to this form of professional co-operation there is a growing recognition that both agencies and professions need to develop a consultancy function (Mills 1979, Kadushin 1977). This function has been variously defined; very widely by some to include all discussions between professionals with the view to producing better work (Mills 1979), and more narrowly by others to describe a situation in which a professional who is consulted gives his advice and help to the consultee who then carries out his own professional task with hopefully new enlightenment (Caplan 1959). It is this narrower definition that we are taking. We consider less-specific discussions to be 'liaison'.

We begin the chapter with some comments on communication, discuss liaison and consultancy in relation to various other professions, and end with a discussion of the need for specialist child guidance agencies to develop a consultancy function.

Communication

The occasions when a social worker has to communicate with members of her own and other professions are numerous. There are also many times when ideally communication should take place, but the channels of communication are closed either because no attempts have been made before, or because previous attempts have ended in failure. Profitable communication does not just happen, and it is often useful to have a regular point of contact. This may take the form of a regular telephone call or case-conference concerning a particular child, or, in an agency, a regular supervision group with an outside professional such as a psychiatrist or a lawyer, to which difficulties can be brought. In this way, a common language can begin to emerge.

Writing about consultancy, Kadushin (1977:145) stresses the importance of the quality of communication between consultee and consultant, and points out the necessity of a clear exposition of the problem. There seems to be three main pitfalls which are also relevant to all inter and intra-professional communications. Firstly, the social worker has to be aware of the differences in language between herself and the person she consults or advises, and she should not be afraid to question points she does not understand. Secondly, the problem is often presented from a very limited perspective because the social worker really believes she already knows the exact nature of the problem. When seeking a consultation, we must be open to the possibility of having our views changed. This can, of course, be very threatening. Thirdly, and almost a paradox of the previous pitfall, is the tendency to present a cascade of information which only serves to confuse the 'consultant'. It takes effort and practice to sit down and organize one's thoughts in a way that is meaningful for others. In Chapter 3 we have outlined what we consider to be a good case-summary which would also be suitable for presentation at a case discussion or to a consultant when seeking advice. In the latter case, it would be necessary to stress the particular area, for example, a legal or medical problem, on which guidance is needed.

Working with teachers

School is a vitally important part of a child's life. He not only acquires knowledge there, but also social skills and experience of peer and adult relationships. It may be in school that the child exhibits problem behaviour which has its roots in difficulties at home. On the other hand, failure to acquire basic learning skills such as reading or writing may lead to major emotional and behavioural problems which, in turn, may prevent the acquisition of learning (Chess and Hassibi 1978: 437). The problems of home and school are interlinked but communications between parents and teachers are often bad and frequently hampered by differences in culture (Sussenwein 1976). As one answer to this problem, some schools have found it useful to have an outside consultant (usually a social worker, psychologist, or psychiatrist) to advise and help with particular problems, including how to communicate with and help parents. One of the consultant's initial tasks is to allay any false expectations of what he is able to do, and to put into perspective any fears that he may be critical of the school's achievements (Moore 1961). The consultant may have dis-cussions with parents (some of whom would be totally unprepared to accept a clinic appointment). Other forms of help offered may include attendance at staff groups to discuss particular problems and general principles, and perhaps observation of a particular child in the classroom, showing the teacher how to make behavioural obser-vations and useful interventions (see Chapter 8). Gorell Barnes (1975b) describes the use of school-based groups, led by social workers, for the parents of disadvantaged children. This school consultancy work is well-developed in some child guidance clinics. A clinic with a staff of six could provide a weekly school-based consultation service for twelve schools by each person allocating one day per week to such a service. This could be a useful way for local authority social services departments to build up relationships with schools. Some schools have counsellors, who may or may not work in an education welfare or social services department, who usually take on some of these consultancy tasks as well as being directly available to children and parents.

However, working in schools is by no means an easy task and unfortunately communications between a social worker and a teacher is often over a particularly difficult child who arouses all kinds of feelings in both. It is necessary for the outsider to appreciate both the needs of the educational institution and the fact that the child concerned is only one of many for whom the teacher·has responsibility. The teacher and the social worker may have very different ideas about what constitutes a problem; for example, a quiet withdrawn child may be a relief to a teacher with a boisterous class. The 'languages' they speak may be different and they must learn to understand one another's language. All this requires motivation, patience, and persistence on the part of those involved.

Working with general practitioners

It is an unfortunate fact that there is often a climate of mutual suspicion and ambivalence between social workers and general practitioners (Huntington 1976). This can only have an adverse effect on the well-being of children whose care may be shared by them. However, numerous studies (for example, Goldberg and Neill 1972, Wilson 1976) have shown the need for and the value of social worker – general practitioner liaison. Huntington (1976) points out the various areas of general practice in which the social worker can have a useful function; (i) in the assessment of a case, (ii) liaising with those involved, (iii) in taking on a therapeutic role, (iv) in supporting the general practitioner in his work, and, (v) in educating him in relevant areas. It is clear that the more interested a general practitioner is in psychiatry (and social aspects of his patients) the more sympathetic he is likely to be to the social worker (Harwin *et al.* 1970). The social worker must also be sympathetic to the general practitioner and bear in mind several points. She must remember that the general practitioner may have 3000 patients, and also allow for his preoccupation with medical aspects of a case. She must avoid the use of jargon which seems to be a particular irritant to doctors, and in all communications she should outline the aims of her involvement and convey her views clearly. An eminent paediatrician once said, 'It is high time the paediatrician and the child psychiatrist married, if only for the sake of the children' (Apley 1968: 30). Much the same might be said for the social worker and general practitioner.

Working with paediatricians

Physical illness is not the only problem to be tackled in a children's ward, for any illness produces stresses for all members of the family. Indeed, 20–30 per cent of children with chronic or episodic illnesses or handicap have some measure of emotional disturbance (Rutter, Tizard and Whitmore 1970) and children with neurological illness have twice that incidence. In addition, there are certain physical conditions where the emotional component is particularly strong (see pp. 81–3).

Despite this, the role of the social worker on the paediatric ward has in the past been very peripheral. Bingley and her colleagues (1980) stress that if a social worker is to be effective she must have a clearly defined role and be accepted as an equal. To achieve this, she must be firmly based within a team and meet regularly with them, rather than being called in at a moment of crisis, or being asked to deal with one particular case. Although the social worker may work directly with families alone or with other members of the team, she should have a strong consultative function, pointing out social and emotional aspects of cases and enabling other members of the team to address themselves to this aspect of the patient's problem. She also needs to be continually aware of the paediatrician's conceptual framework, which like the general practitioner's, differs dramatically from her own.

Working with lawyers

The statutory powers and duties possessed by local authorities with regard to children, places on them a huge responsibility. The welfare of a great many children depends upon this power being used wisely. The law and the underlying issues have become more complex, especially since the Children's Act 1975, and individuals have become more aware of their rights to challenge authority (Adcock and White 1979–80). Increasingly, the social worker relies on the lawyer. However, her training differs considerably. Adcock and White point out that social workers are concerned with ideas and feelings and lawyers with facts and decisions, and that neither approach on its own is likely to result in the most effective help for children and their families. Obviously these two approaches need to be combined.

Of course, the quality and quantity of the legal support provided by a local authority is an important factor and at the moment this varies considerably from one authority to another. Few lawyers are experienced in children's law and we would like to see more employed in this area full-time. However, there is a large onus on the social worker to help build up a mutually trusting relationship with the lawyer and to present clearly the important issues in a particular case. To be most effective, lawyers should be involved at the beginning of a case and not just as a crisis occurs. This not only enables him to understand the case more fully, but also allows opportunity to seek more general legal advice about the advisability of different courses of action before the point of crisis. Such a facility is rarely available, but unless social workers make the demands the extent of the need can not be known.

The responsibility for making the final decision about what action is best to take lies with the social worker. If she has presented the issues clearly to the lawyer, he should be able to advise on the legal aspects. Success depends on a mutual respect for, and understanding of each other's professional skills.

The consultancy role of a child guidance clinic

The child guidance clinic and, similarly, child psychiatric departments, have within them a great deal of expertise and yet until recently this was not made readily available or used by other agencies (such as social services departments). Such clinics can only hope to meet the needs of a small proportion of those who might benefit from help (Scott et al. 1976). Some clinics like the one in Dunstable (Mills

1979) are giving a central role to a consultancy service and we are certain that this policy should be widely extended. There is an onus on the clinics to reach out to the community and on other agencies to make clear how they would find the clinics useful to them in carrying out their work.

Throughout this chapter we stress the importance of different professions having respect for one another; this respect is often not present between clinic and community workers. Those in the clinic often regard those outside as 'not doing proper work', and those outside often regard those inside as 'out of touch with the stress of social work' (Lloyd-Davies 1960). It is only by an increased sharing and awareness of each other's different function that these prejudices can be overcome. There are a number of ways in which a consultancy function might be carried out.

(1) Discussion of referrals. So often a social worker, general practitioner, or teacher is unsure whether or not to refer a child or family. By discussing each referral with the referral agent, not only is continuity of work more likely but many referrals might be directed to more appropriate places.

(2) Consultation meetings. These could range from large case conferences to a meeting between two workers; their function may vary from deciding on a joint strategy to a more directly educative role. On a psychiatric team with which one of us was involved, each week there was an open meeting to which outside workers (of any kind) could come and discuss cases. Sometimes the result was a referral to the clinic and at other times the visiting worker would just gain advice and support. Short-term help was given more quickly and social workers did not have to wait months, only to learn that nothing could be done or that they were doing the right thing anyway. Such meetings also helped the staff of the clinic to operate with a greater awareness of the outside world.

Meetings should not, of course, always be in the clinic. One of us took part in a successful group held in a social services department area office and run by a local child psychiatrist. This was held not only to discuss individual cases but also to discuss general principles and difficulties.

Earlier we have discussed members of a child psychiatric team visiting schools in a consultative capacity; community and children's homes can be visited in the same way.

(3) Occasional conferences and seminars. These are useful injections of learning but real consultation and liaison must be carried out on a regular basis.

(4) Working together. A great many cases dealt with by a child guidance clinic have other workers involved. Continual contact and liaison with the taking of joint decisions (where there is agreement) are important. Co-therapy, with a local authority and clinic worker seeing a family together can be a useful strategy, reducing the possibility of the family splitting the respective workers, and allowing a more comprehensive view of the problem. Objections have been raised to such an approach, and as with all co-therapy, there is a need for the therapists to have an honest open relationship. One issue commonly raised is that of confidentiality, but as with all decisions to share information, except in very special circumstances, this should only be done with the permission of the parents or family.

The question of ultimate responsibility also might arise. Obviously, if one worker has statutory obligations with regard to a case the final responsibility must be hers, but in a case where there is a medical problem, such as in anorexia nervosa, that responsibility belongs to the doctor. In most situations, however, the final responsibility rests with the family.

Conclusions

Social workers, together with their colleagues, need to examine more carefully their relationships with other professionals, and to improve the quality of their communications. To achieve this, it is necessary for them to have confidence in their capabilities, to respect and attempt to understand other professions, and to accept that they all need each other, for no profession can hope to encompass all the knowledge and skills necessary to help children and families with problems.

10
Environmental change and alternative forms of care

Environmental change

In Chapters 2 and 3 we discuss ways in which aspects of the environment outside the family can cause or aggravate child-focused problems. Sometimes direct work with the family or particular family members helps them to tackle environmental problems themselves. However, the social worker must be prepared to work directly with environmental factors on behalf of clients and client groups, and in this chapter we discuss those areas particularly relevant to the disturbed child and his family.

As a basis for this work, not only must the social worker develop particular skills, but also acquire a sound knowledge of the area in which she works and the resource-systems within it. To assist her, it is essential that every agency builds up a comprehensive resource file, regularly up-dated and readily available to workers.

EDUCATION

When considering possible changes in the educational environment, there is a wide spectrum from which to choose. The possibilities include changes in the classroom such as the use of a more (or less) disciplined approach by the teacher, a lessening of academic pressure by the parents, and a change of school, or a special school placement. Sometimes the intervention will seek to remedy a problem in the school and sometimes to provide an environment better suited to a difficult child's needs.

Children with emotional, behavioural, and learning difficulties, and with below normal or borderline intelligence (i.e. IQ less than 75) may have problems coping with normal school, especially if the underlying problems have not been recognized. Some borderline children may cope in a normal school, providing difficulties have been identified and appropriate remedial help given. More intellectually handicapped children are better placed in schools for the educationally subnormal. There are also a few schools for children with very specific difficulties, such as delay in language development.

Children who show behavioural problems in the classroom present a particular difficulty for schools (especially secondary schools). Some schools have provided sanctuary classes or have used remedial classes to contain such children. The same classes are often used to accommodate children who are extremely shy or who for other reasons find school-life difficult. This mix is unsatisfactory and, although the staff-pupil ratio may be good, presents the teachers involved with a difficult task. Certain education authorities have provided special centres to which children with behaviour difficulties can be referred for education, and sometimes social work or psychiatric help are provided. However, such centres are often characterized by a high turnover of staff, and there is no evidence that they provide a successful solution to the problem. The advantage of course is that ordinary school classes are freed of some of their more difficult children.

For children whom ordinary schools find it impossible to contain, placement in a school for maladjusted children may be the necessary solution. Such schools can be day or boarding and may vary considerably in approach. The advantages of such a placement is the high staff-pupil ratio, the special educational help, and the acceptance of, and skilled help for, the child's difficulties. There are obvious disadvantages in taking a child out of the ordinary school system and any decision should be made on the basis of the child's needs.

There is a number of special schools for the 'delicate' or mildly physically handicapped. These may cater for a variety of problems or for a specific handicap such as asthma or epilepsy.

Referral for special schooling can be a lengthy procedure usually carried out by the educational psychologist. Referrals for schools for the maladjusted must also include reports from a psychiatrist and a social worker. Families need support and help throughout the whole process of placement and this should be continued afterwards even if the placement is at a boarding-school. Laslett (1977) provides a useful review of the education of disturbed children.

In Chapter 9 we discuss some of the difficulties of working with schools.

HOUSING

There is no doubt that poor housing does contribute towards child-hood disturbance (p. 20) and in cases where this is evident, whether it be the effect of high-rise living (Jephcott 1971), overcrowding (Mitchell 1971), or generally poor conditions, every effort should be made to effect a change. Work on behalf of the client may involve liaison with the relevant housing department and making as good a case as possible for re-housing. Needless to say, this is usually a time-consuming and depressing task. Alternatively, such work may involve guiding a client through tenants' rights legislation to afford an improvement in housing conditions. When considering the possible effects of re-housing, it must be borne in mind that re-housing can be severely disruptive if it breaks up friendships and established community networks (Fried 1963). Housing satisfaction does seem to be associated with a sense of identification with an area and sometimes a client who requests frequent housing-moves, com-plaining of a bad neighbourhood or neighbours, really needs help in building up a network within the community.

If a particular area produces a high incidence of referral for help, it is important to examine the reasons, enlisting the assistance of local community workers, tenants' associations, or other groups. Ameni-ties such as open spaces, safe play facilities, and access to shops, are very important to the life of the community as well as to particular families, and where a social worker is aware that lack of these is contributing to problems, she should be involved in pressing for their provision.

POVERTY

Poverty is so bound up with other factors such as poor housing, low educational attainment, and low social status that it is difficult to assess its individual contribution to childhood disturbance. However, it seems safe to assume that any alleviation of poverty and its effects constitutes a positive intervention. The causes of poverty are many and although the individual social worker can contribute her knowledge and experience to the understanding of and fight against poverty her aims in individual cases usually have to be more modest.

Clients who are dependent on unemployment or social security benefits often need help in negotiating their full entitlements, and this advocacy role is a crucial one for social workers. Managing on a small amount of money is a very difficult task and many families need help in working out their priorities. If debts occur the social worker can help by negotiating the repayments and preventing children in the family suffering from such effects as cut-off electricity.

The social worker, limited in the money she has available to help directly, finds much of her work is negotiating with others on behalf of her client. Local authorities vary in their provision of money and material help under Section 1 of the Children and Young Persons Act 1963, and in our opinion many authorities interpret it too narrowly. Charities are a good source of money for a particular item such as a washing machine or electric fire and various charities and organizations provide holidays both for children and families. These kinds of interventions are small in comparison to the total effects of poverty but can be of great importance to a particular family.

SUPPORT GROUPS

(a) National organizations

Disillusionment with the existing helping services has led to a growth in the self-help movement (Robinson and Henry 1977) and certainly many organizations both nationally and through local groups can be of great assistance to families with particular needs. They usually have the experience and detailed knowledge that is often unavailable in the statutory services. It is impossible to list all the groups that might be helpful to clients, but some of those which in our experience have proved particularly helpful are the Down's Children's Association, the National Association for Autistic Children, Gingerbread (for one-parent families), Parents Anonymous (for those parents afraid they might physically abuse a child), Cruse (national organization for bereaved families), Prisoners' Wives and Families' Association, and the National Association for the Mentally Handicapped. A more comprehensive list with addresses can be found in the Family Welfare Association's *Guide to the Social Services 1980*.

(b) Local groups

There are many local groups which can offer support to all the family or individual members, including those groups which are part of national organizations. This support function may only be incidental to their main remit. Such groups include pre-school playgroups, one o'clock clubs, mother-and-toddler groups, local authority afternoon and evening classes, Housewives Register, The National Childbirth Trust, Boy Scouts, Girl Guides, drama and youth groups, etc. There are times when involvement in a support group of this kind can be crucial in helping parents or children to cope.

CASE ILLUSTRATIONS

The first case illustrates the way in which a simple intervention can have wide ranging effects and the second illustrates the variety of environmental interventions that is sometimes indicated.

Elaine's father, deserted by her mother and left to cope with four young children, was introduced by her social worker to a local group of Gingerbread. The result was that he regained a social life and received help and support in bringing up his children, whilst Elaine, 9, who had taken on the role of surrogate mother, was able to return to school and regain her own peer-group relationships.

Louise, aged 4, was referred to the social services department by the health visitor because she was depressed and uncommunicative. It was immediately apparent that the family problems were more widespread. Louise and her three younger sisters lived with their West Indian mother in two damp, cold, and tiny privately rented rooms. The property was in terrible repair and the roof leaked in the bedroom. Mother had given up trying to cope under difficult conditions. She had become depressed and was claiming only her basic social security payments. There was little money for food and clothes so the family remained at home. All the children were incontinent and the rooms smelt of urine. Mother was able to respond to the social worker's offers of support and help. The public health inspectors were contacted and their report on the property, and lack of action by the landlord eventually led to re-housing. New mattresses, bed-linen, and a laundry service were provided. Help was given in claiming from the Department of Health and Social Security and a grant obtained for heating and clothes. The older children were found places in a local playgroup, and mother was encouraged to join a local mother-and-toddlers group. The whole family responded to this support and improvement in their life, and mother again began to make decisions for herself. The children became more lively and made friends at playgroup. Although the family needed continuing help over the following year, it did not return to its previously depressed state.

Alternative forms of care

Alternative forms of care range from daily child-minding to a long-term fostering or children's home placement. They may seek to provide an alternative to family life or a therapeutic milieu with specific aims for helping the child and his family. The placement may be made in response to a request by the family or at times against the wishes of the family. Whatever the circumstances, a well-thought-out decision must be made about the kind of care required, the effects on the family, and the kind of help that needs to be provided.

IN-PATIENT PSYCHIATRIC CARE

In-patient units are of value for only a small proportion of children with difficulties and only when the child and his family have not responded to other forms of help (Hersov and Bentovim 1976). Units vary considerably in their facilities and general approach and a full and useful account of the in-patient treatment of different problems and an examination of the work of different units is provided by Barker (1974).

Social workers and doctors in the community often express frustration that in-patient units fail to provide the kind of service the community needs. This is partly due to unreal expectations of what is, and probably should be, a limited service. Apart from children with acute psychotic episodes or suicidal behaviour, emergencies are usually not admitted and the facility should not be used as an alternative to other, more relevant, forms of treatment, residential care, or educational provision. The kinds of children who would benefit from admission are: (a) those whose thought and behaviour is so bizarre that they cannot be coped with on an out-patient basis and those who constitute a danger to themselves or others, (b) those whose socially unacceptable behaviour arises from a degree of disorder which is unaffected by ordinary social measures or out-patient treatment, (c) those whose complex problems require skilled observation, assessment, and treatment on a continuous and intense basis not possible as an out-patient, (d) those whose family interaction is so distorted that life at home leads to a continuing or progressive interference with the child's development and progress (Hersov and Bentovim 1976).

It is necessary to be sure that in-patient care as such is indicated and that foster care or a children's home placement would not provide a better alternative. There is always the danger that admission to an in-patient unit may lead to the further exclusion from the family of an already 'scapegoated' child and that the sick role of the referred child is underlined and maintained. One solution to this is to admit the whole family (Nakhla, Folkart, and Webster, 1969) and in our view although this may not always be practical, a family approach should always be taken to in-patient care.

A full range of therapeutic techniques should be available to help those children whose problems are so complex or severe that hospitalization is necessary. Admission and discharge are crucial stages in in-patient help and families should be given a realistic idea of in-patient provision and what to expect from it. Families may need special help in receiving a child home again. Day-patients are accepted in a number of in-patient units (Barker 1974), and day-patient status can prove a useful transition prior to discharge.

DAY-HOSPITALS AND DAY-CENTRES

The terms 'day-hospital' and 'day-centre' are in most cases interchangeable but differ from other day-care facilities such as nurseries and schools in that the therapeutic role is the central one (Laufer, Laffey, and Davidson 1974). The majority of day-centres are in medical settings but rely heavily on non-medical personnel and use a multidisciplinary team approach (Hersov and Bentovim 1976). Some local authorities have set up day-centres for mothers and children, and families, and we consider that for the majority of the problems this is a more appropriate setting. Day-centres may be part of an in-patient or other residential setting, or may be entirely separate.

Day-centres have obvious advantages over in-patient units, in that contact with the family and community is maintained as well as being less costly. Although initially they were set up to provide for children who were less disturbed than those needing residential help, it has been argued that they provide a more effective service even for the most disturbed children (Devlin 1962), and Atkins (1962) has claimed equal success for more disturbed children, using either day-hospital or in-patient treatment. D'Amato (1969) observed that where day provision exists, the demand for residential help diminishes.

A whole range of problems can be dealt with on a day-centre basis, although children with anti-social behaviour, psychotic disorders, and severe speech and language disorders do less well (Hersov and Bentovim 1976). Young children seem to do better than older children and many provisions are for the under-five's.

We consider family involvement essential in day-centre help and stress the necessity to state clear goals, formulated jointly by day-centre workers and those in the community who will continue care after discharge. Gold and Reisman's follow-up study (1970) indicates the need for longer-term special education facilities or continued treatment after attendance at a day-centre. Obviously, attendance must be seen as just the basis for a variety of necessary interventions.

NURSERIES AND CHILD-MINDERS

It is often necessary and appropriate for small children to be looked after during the day by someone outside the family. When there are particular stresses and problems within the family, it is especially important that the alternative care is good. In ordinary circumstances child-minders have an extremely difficult task (Jackson and Jackson 1979) and will need extra support and help with any child who has special difficulties.

REMOVAL OF CHILD FROM HOME

In extreme circumstances, it sometimes becomes necessary for a child (with or without his siblings) to be removed from his own home. There are many reasons why this action might be taken. Sometimes it is done informally with full parental permission, although resources are so scarce that this sort of action is often impossible except in cases which demand legislative backing (Children and Young Persons Act 1969). The reasons for the removal of a child have usually given rise to emotional difficulties, but the process of removal often adds to the difficulties, especially as this is frequently done in a hurry in a period of crisis. Family members and helping professionals are often forced into extreme positions, and a great deal of effort is needed to work-through all the feelings generated. In addition, the standards of alternative care can be low, and add to the burdens that the child has to cope with.

Therefore, it is evident that removal from home is a measure to be taken only when all other interventions have failed, or seem very likely to fail. The most common forms of alternative care are foster-care and children's home.

(a) Foster-care

Fostering any child is a difficult task, and when the child has particular difficulties the rate of breakdown is high (Wolkind 1978). One response to this has been the setting-up of a professional fostering service, in which the foster-parents are paid a salary and provided with extensive back-up support. An example is the Kent Family Placement Project (Hazel 1977) and the indications are that this and other projects, including a growing number in the United States and Canada, provide a useful alternative to institutional help. One characteristic of these projects is the continuing help given to the child's natural family, and in any fostering placement this seems to be a crucial area of work. The natural family also experiences trauma and loss (Jenkins 1969) and if the original difficulties are not tackled, it is unlikely that a return home will succeed. Often a child gradually loses contact with his natural parents and it has been suggested that the existence of continued contacts with parents is a useful predictor of a positive outcome for the child (Kufeld 1979).

(b) Children's homes

Although the trend for some time has been towards smaller family group homes, larger institutions still remain (King, Raynes, and Tizard 1971). This is not the place to discuss in detail the character of this form of provision, except to state our conviction that provision is too limited, occasionally geographically misplaced, and often staffed with ill-trained or inexperienced workers coping under impossible circumstances to meet the needs of a very difficult group of clients. Staff turnover is high, yet evidence has shown that contact with the same housemother for two years is associated with a lower rate of psychiatric disorder (Wolkind 1977). There has been much concern about the effect of institutional care and certainly there is a high incidence of disturbance found in children's homes. Tizard and Rees (1975) suggest that this is not related to early institutional care *per se*, but to poor quality care and contact with the child's own disturbed family. Wolkind (1974a) points out that the answer does not lie in returning the child to his family at all costs, but it is also necessary to identify factors in the institutional environment that may lead to further damage.

Community psychiatric and social work services need to be more active in providing support for children's homes and advice on a consultative basis, as well as in relation to individual cases.

Conclusions

As in other forms of intervention, clear aims must be formulated so that the success or otherwise of environmental changes can be monitored. The kinds of help discussed in this chapter belong within a wide spectrum of possible interventions and should be considered in every case. There is little point in, for instance, expecting a mother to undertake behaviour modification techniques with her children when she is finding it impossible to cope with the basic problem of feeding and clothing them. However, it is important to remain aware that even in families where there is great deprivation, it may be a relationship problem that is causing a difficulty such as school-refusal or encopresis and not the family's other problems. All aspects of a family's functioning must be considered.

11

Medication

Introduction

Drug treatment has only limited value in the management of child-hood psychological disorders. There is minimal evidence as to its effectiveness, and drug research with children is more difficult than with adults for a variety of legal, ethical, and psychiatric reasons. These points notwithstanding, medication is widely used, often quite inappropriately. The careful assessment and correct treatment of childhood problems is complex and time-consuming, and it is all too tempting to take the short-cut of prescribing such drugs as tranquillizers or anti-depressants. (The same point applies in adult life, and it is probably not an exaggeration to state that of all drugs, tranquillizers and anti-depressants are the most mis-used, both by doctors and patients.)

Ideally, the following principles should be adhered to in the use of drugs for treating childhood disorders: (1) drugs should be prescribed only after a detailed assessment of the situation, which should include a family interview and a school report. (2) Drugs should be used to treat specific symptoms rather than a specific disorder. No drug has been shown to be of value to all children with a specific disorder. (3) There should always be a clearly defined reason for the use of drugs, and a specified length of treatment after which the situation should be reviewed. (4) Other aspects of management should always be associated with drug prescription. (5) Parental consent and co-operation is essential. Ambivalence, uncertainty, and fear of side-effects or addiction may all militate against the effectiveness of the drug or even its regular use. Time should be spent explaining the purpose of the medication, the length of time for which it will be prescribed, the possible side-effects, and the action to be taken should side-effects occur. Parents should be given every opportunity to discuss all these considerations.

Hypnotics (sleeping medicines)

Hypnotics have a useful part to play in the management of sleep disorders in young children (pp. 69–70). A small dose used for a short period may be sufficient to break a faulty sleep pattern. The mild hypnotics such as chloral, Phenergan or Vallergan are all safe (these latter two are actually anti-histamines but have an hypnotic effect). In older children and adolescents with severe sleep disturbance, hypnotics are best avoided, but if medication is essential then diazepam (Valium) or nitrazepam (Mogadon) may be used for a *short* time. There is no place at all for the use of barbiturates in sleep disturbance in adults or children. They have powerful side-effects and are addictive. Night-terrors (p. 70) often respond well to diazepam.

Mild tranquillizers and sedatives

These include such drugs as diazepam, chlordiazepoxide (Librium) and are of most value in conditions associated with anxiety (p. 55). They may also have a part to play in the treatment of obsessional disorders (p. 60).

Major tranquillizers

This range of drugs includes chlorpromazine (Largactil), trifluoperazine (Stelazine) and haloperidol (Serenace). They are used predominantly for very severe problems such as schizophrenia (p. 68) and hyperkinetic syndrome (p. 77). Haloperidol is often of value in the treatment of tics and Gilles de la Tourette syndrome (p. 80).

Antidepressants

There are two major types of antidepressants: tricyclics and mono-amine-oxidase-inhibitors (MAOI). There is no place whatsoever for the use of the MAOI's in childhood despite Frommer's contrary but unsubstantiated claims (1972). They are potentially dangerous and no more need be said. The tricyclic antidepressants such as imipramine (Tofranil) or amitryptyline (Tryptizol) are occasionally used in the treatment of childhood depression (pp. 58–9) and nocturnal enuresis (p. 174). They have unpleasant though generally not dangerous side-effects and should therefore be used sparingly.

Stimulants

This range of drugs is used to improve attention and concentration in hyperkinetic children. This paradoxical effect of stimulants seeming to have a depressant effect is probably due to the fact that they stimulate that part of the brain concerned with inhibiting activity. The most commonly prescribed are the amphetamines and methylphenidate (Ritalin), both of which are undoubtedly helpful for such symptoms, although they do not alter the course of the underlying disorder. They do have side-effects and there is a risk of addiction.

Lithium

Treatment of manic-depressive illnesses with lithium has proved to be one of the major advances in psychiatry this century. This illness is rare in childhood (p. 68) but where it does occur, lithium may well modify the condition. Lithium usage has to be very carefully monitored, and regular blood tests are mandatory. Occasionally, lithium has been reported to be of value as a mood-stabilizer in children with hyperkinetic syndrome.

Anticonvulsants

This range of drugs is used in the treatment of various forms of epilepsy. The most commonly-prescribed anticonvulsants are barbiturates such as phenobarbitone, primidone (Mysoline), sulthiame (Ospolot), phenytoin (Epanutin), sodium valproate (Epilim), and carbamazepine (Tegretol). All have side-effects including irritability and sleepiness. Children with epilepsy and other forms of brain-damage frequently suffer behaviour disturbances for which sulthiame is said to be of particular value.

CONCLUSIONS

Medication is of limited value despite its frequent use, and should only be used in association with other forms of management. Care should be taken to ensure that the parents understand the reasons for the use of medication, and are in agreement with it.

Case illustration

As a way of attempting to summarize some of what has been said we include this brief case illustration presented in chronological sequence, and highlighting the essential aspects of the background, assessment, and management. We emphasize the central role of the social worker amidst a myriad of helping professionals, the importance of a clear formulation and management plan, and the use of a range of carefully co-ordinated interventions.

Background

The W. family consists of Laura, aged 31; her second husband, Ken, 27; Martin, 10; Alan, 9; and Sam, 8; children of Laura's first marriage, and Christine, aged 1½. The family have been well known to the local social services department for a variety of reasons; there had been protracted proceedings over the custody of the boys who eventually had been made wards of court; the family live in inadequate accommodation and had made repeated requests for rehousing; Laura suffers from frequent bouts of depression and occasional convulsions necessitating hospitalization, and emergency arrangements for the care of the children. The family's troubles have recently been exacerbated by Ken being made redundant. Shortly after this, the school referred Martin to child guidance because of disruptive behaviour in the classroom. It had also been noted that Alan had frequent episodes of abdominal pain, Sam was overactive, and Christine was both short and underweight for her age.

Assessment

The psychiatrist arranged for a whole family assessment, and asked the family's local authority social worker if she could also attend in view of her detailed knowledge of the family. School reports were obtained and the general practitioner's view was sought regarding Laura's epilepsy, Alan's abdominal pain, and Christine's failure to thrive. After having a joint meeting with the family and their social worker, sharing views with her, and studying all the reports, the psychiatrist made the following formulation:

Formulation

This family has considerable problems arising both from external sources and as a result of its own dysfunction. The redundancy and inadequate housing are major burdens for a family that is unable to use its own resources at the best of times to cope with daily stresses. Their major weakness is the inability of Laura and Ken to recognize each other's distress and provide mutual support. Ken feels hopelessly inadequate and overwhelmed by the demands of an 'instant family', and consequently withdraws. Laura, who desperately needs Ken to be strong and assertive, is unable to express her resentment and subsequently feels depressed. Neither is able to cope with the other, their reactions exacerbate the difficulties, and both are unable to cope with the children's needs and demands. Martin's disruptiveness at school is likely to be a reaction to the stresses at home, although it should be noted that he is almost three years behind in reading; this is certain to be a contributory factor, whether the delay is due to a specific reading difficulty or an emotionally determined underachievement. It is probable that Alan's abdominal pain and Christine's failure to thrive are somatized responses to stress and distress, and it is possible that Laura's convulsions have similar triggering factors. Sam's overactivity appears to be a reaction to a lack of attention and stimulation at home, because, providing he is in a structured setting, such as school, he is fairly settled. Considerable effort will be required to help this family, but such an input is justified as further disruptions and separations are likely to have a devastating effect on each member of the family.

Management

Interventions in a number of different areas are necessary:

(I)   COLLECTION OF FURTHER INFORMATION

(a) Laura has previously been seen by a neurologist, who should be consulted regarding the possible organic causes for the convulsions, and the necessity for the current anti-convulsant medication which may be contributing to her depression.
(b) Alan has been seen by a paediatrician, who should be consulted as to the likelihood of a psychogenic basis for the abdominal pain. A definitive statement to this effect may help relieve the family's anxiety about possible serious illness.
(c) The same applies to Christine but she has not yet been seen by a paediatrician. This should be arranged.
(d) An assessment is required of Martin's intellectual skills to ascertain the cause of his reading retardation, and his remedial requirements.

(II)   FAMILY-BASED INTERVENTIONS

(a) The predominant need of this family is the ability to acknowledge and share concerns, and provide mutual support. They could be helped with this through meetings for the whole family or just the parents.
(b) The parents require, in addition, advice on management of the children's physical and behaviour problems.

(III)   ENVIRONMENTAL CHANGES

The family would benefit from rehousing, and Ken requires help in finding another job. Martin may need remedial help at school, dependent upon the outcome of his psychological assessment. Laura should be advised on local facilities for very young children and their mothers.

(IV)   LIAISON

In view of the large number of professionals concerned, careful liaison is necessary to co-ordinate care and avoid overlapping and/or contradictory advice and management. Whilst a case-conference might help in this respect, it is unlikely that all those concerned would be able to meet at the same time. Further, most of them are likely to remain involved for a lengthy period. Consequently, it seems more important to have a key worker who co-ordinates all the different aspects of management and ensures a satisfactory communication network between the professionals. The local authority social worker is the person best able to fulfil this role.

Process

(I) INFORMATION

(a) The neurologist has been unable to find an organic cause for Laura's convulsions and thinks it quite possible that there is a psychogenic basis. He has agreed to a change of medication to a type with a less depressant effect.

(b) The paediatrician has confirmed that there is no organic basis to Alan's abdominal pain and agreed to a joint meeting with the social worker and parents to explain this.

(c) The same paediatrician has seen Christine and considered her failure to thrive to have no physical cause.

(d) Psychological assessment shows Martin's intelligence to be within the normal range, but that he has a marked lack of confidence and associated anxiety during testing. The psychologist recommends that he should receive some remedial help for reading.

(II) FAMILY-BASED INTERVENTIONS

The psychiatrist and social worker have arranged a series of six joint meetings with the parents. Therapy is focused on (a) the inadequate communication between the parents as characterized by their inability to share their concerns and provide mutual support, and (b) the issues relating to the management of the children. The therapeutic setting enables both parents to start expressing disappointment in the other, and specifying how each would like the other to be. Communication between them has gradually become more open, and they have begun to learn how to work together and support each other in the management of the children, adopting a consistent and coherent policy, instead of the previous haphazard and inconsistent responses to the children's needs.

(III) ENVIRONMENTAL CHANGES

Ken is attending a government re-training programme. Martin is attending a remedial reading class in his school. A series of letters have been sent by various professionals involved to the housing department. Laura takes Christine to a mother-and-toddler's club three mornings a week.

(IV) LIAISON

The social worker has taken a central role in overall management. She has fortnightly discussions with the general practitioner, and similarly keeps in touch with the various school teachers. Any concerns are discussed and solutions sought. When the family therapy had been completed, the social worker telephoned the psychiatrist about once a month to discuss progress. She visits the family home once a fortnight.

Outcome

Nine months after the initial referral to child-guidance, there have been considerable improvements. Martin's behaviour at school is no longer a concern, and he is only one year behind in reading. Alan's abdominal pains occur infrequently. Sam is no longer considered to be overactive, and Christine has begun to catch up on growth although she is still somewhat small for her age. Ken is more assertive and forthcoming, though still lacking in confidence to some degree. He has completed his re-training scheme and has just started a new job. Laura has had no further fits and whilst still having 'bad days', no longer has bouts of depression. She continues to take a small dose of an anticonvulsant, and it is hoped to stop this shortly. The family have not yet been rehoused!

References

Ackerman, N. (1966) *Treating the Troubled Family*. New York: Basic Books.

Adams, P. (1974) *A Primer of Child Psychotherapy*. Boston: Little Brown.

Adcock, M. and White, R. (1979–80) Lawyers, Social Workers and Children. In *Concern* (National Children's Bureau) **34**: 19–23.

Aitken, P. (1978) Ten to Fourteen year-olds and Alcohol. Volume III. London: HMSO.

Alexander, J. and Parsons, B. (1973) Short-term Behavioral Intervention with Delinquent Families: Impact on Family Process and Recidivism. *Journal of Abnormal Psychology* **81**: 219–25.

Andolfi, M. (1979) *Family Therapy – An Interactional Approach*. New York and London: Plenum.

Anthony, E. (1957) Group Analytic Psychotherapy with Children and Adolescents. In S. Foulkes and E. Anthony *Group Psychotherapy*. Harmondsworth: Penguin.

Anthony, E. (1970) Behaviour Disorder. In P. Mussen (ed) *Manual of Child Psychology*. London: John Wiley.

Apley, J. (1958) Paediatrics and Child Psychiatry. In E. Miller (ed) *Foundations of Child Psychiatry*. Oxford: Pergamon.

Atkins, T. (1962) *Criteria for the Differential Use of Treatment Settings for Children with Emotional Disorders*. New York: Child Welfare League of America.

Baird, P. (1978) The Evaluation of Social Work Practice. In *The Unitary Model*. Birmingham University Social Work Studies: British Association of Social Work.

Baker, H. and Wills, U. (1979) School Phobic Children at Work. *British Journal of Psychiatry* **135**: 561–64.

Bancroft, J. (1968) Homosexuality in the Male. *British Journal of Hospital Medicine*. February: 183.

Bandura, A. (1969) *Principles of Behavior Modification*. New York: Holt, Rinehart, and Winston.

—— (1974) Behaviour Theory and the Models of Man. *Journal of Psychology* **29**: 859–69.

Bandura, A. and Walters, R. (1963) *Social Learning and Personality Development*. New York: Holt, Rinehart, and Winston.

Bannister, D. and Fransella, F. (1971) *Inquiring Man – The Theory of Personal Constructs*. Harmondsworth: Penguin.

Barker, P. (1974) The Results of In-patient Care. In P. Barker (ed) *The Residential Psychiatric Treatment of Children*. London: Crosby, Lockwood and Staples.

—— (1979) *Basic Child Psychiatry*. London: Crosby, Lockwood and Staples.

Barnes, G. (1973) Working with the Family Group. *Social Work Today* **3**: 4.

Barnes, J. and Lucas, H. (1974) Positive Discrimination in Education. In T. Leggat (ed) *Sociological Theory and Survey Research*. Beverley Hills, California: Sage Publications.

Bateson, G., Jackson, D., Haley, J., and Weakland, J. (1956) Towards a Theory of Schizophrenia. *Behavioral Science* **I**: 251–64.

Becker, W., Madsen, C., Arnold, C., and Thomas, D. (1967) The Contingent Use of Teacher Attention and Praise in Reducing Classroom Problems. *Journal of Special Education* **I**: 287–307.

Beels, C. and Ferber, A. (1969) Family Therapy – A view. *Family Process* **8**: 280–318.

Bentovim, A. (1973) Disturbed and Under Five. *Special Education* **62**: 31–6.

—— (1978) Family Therapy when the Child is the Referred Patient. In S. Bloch (ed) *Introduction to the Psychotherapies*. Oxford: Oxford University Press.

—— (1979) Theories of Family Interaction and Techniques of Intervention. *Journal of Family Therapy* **1(4)**: 321–45.

Berger, M., Yule, W., and Rutter, M. (1975) Attainment and Adjustment in Two Geographical Areas. *British Journal of Psychiatry* **126**: 510–19.

Berkowitz, I. (1972) *Adolescents Grow in Groups.* London: Butterworths.

Bernal, J. (1973) Night-waking in Infants During the First Fourteen Months. *Developmental Medicine and Child Neurology* **15**: 760–69.

Berry, J. (1972) *Working with Children.* London: Routledge and Kegan Paul.

Bingley, E., Leonard, J., Hensman, S., Lask, B., and Wolff, O. (1980) The Comprehensive Management of Children on a Paediatric Ward – A Family Approach. *Archives of Diseases in Childhood* **55**: 555–61.

Black, D. (1978) The Bereaved Child. *Journal of Child Psychology and Psychiatry* **19(4)**: 287–92.

Blinder, B., Freeman, D., and Stunkard, A. (1970) Behavior Therapy of Anorexia Nervosa. *American Journal of Psychiatry* **126**: 77.

Bloch, D. and La Perriere, K. (1973) Techniques of Family Therapy – A Conceptual Frame. In D. Bloch (ed) *Techniques of Family Therapy – A Primer.* New York: Grune and Stratton.

Blurton-Jones, N., Ferreira, M., Brown, M., and McDonald, L. (1978) The Association Between Perinatal Factors and Later Night-waking. *Developmental Medicine and Child Neurology* **20**: 427–34.

Boszormenyi-Nagy, I. and Spark, G. (1973) *Invisible Loyalties.* New York: Harper and Row.

Bowen, M. (1966) The Use of Family Theory in Clinical Practice. *Comprehensive Psychiatry* **7(5)**: 345–74.

—— (1971) The Use of Family Theory in Clinicial Practice. In J. Haley (ed) *Changing Families.* New York: Grune and Stratton.

Bowlby, J. (1951) *Maternal Care and Mental Health.* Geneva: World Health Organisation.

—— (1975) *Attachment and Loss. Volume II: Separation, Anxiety and Anger.* Harmondsworth: Penguin.

Boxall, M. (1973) Nurture Groups. In *Concern* (National Children's Bureau) No. 12.

Brophy, J. and Good, T. (1974) *Teacher-Student Relationships – Causes and Consequences.* New York: Holt, Rinehart, and Winston.

Bruch, H. (1973) *Eating Disorders: Obesity, Anorexia Nervosa and the*

Person Within. New York: Basic Books.

Byng-Hall, J. (1979) Re-editing Family Mythology during Family Therapy. *Journal of Family Therapy* **I(2):** 103–15.

Caplan, G. (1959) Concepts of Mental Health Consultation. United States Department of Health, Education and Welfare Children's Bureau.

—— (1964) *Principles of Preventive Psychiatry*. New York: Basic Books.

Caplan, H. (1970) Hysterical Conversion Symptoms in Childhood. Master of Philosophy dissertation, University of London.

Carr, A. (1974) Compulsive Neurosis – A Review of the Literature. *Psychological Bulletin* **81**: 311–18.

Carr, J. (1974) The Effect of the Severely Subnormal on their Families. In A. M. Clarke and A. D. B. Clarke (eds) *Mental Deficiency: The Changing Outlook*. Third Edition. London: Methuen.

Chess, S. and Hassibi, A. (1978) *Principles and Practice of Child Psychiatry*. New York: Plenum.

The Children and Young Persons' Act 1969. London: HMSO.

Churven, P. (1978) Families: Parental Attitudes to Family Assessment in a Child Psychiatry Setting. *Journal of Child Psychology and Psychiatry* **19(1)**: 33–42.

Clement, D., Fazzone, R., and Goldstein, B. (1970) Tangible Reinforcers and Child Group Therapy? *Journal of American Academy of Child Psychiatry.* **9**: 409–27.

Coleman, J. (1979) Who Leads Who Astray? Causes of Anti-social Behaviour in Adolescence. *Journal of Adolescence* **2**: 179–86.

Corbett, J., Matthews, A., Connell, P., and Shapiro, D. (1969) Tics and Gilles de la Tourette's Syndrome. *British Journal of Psychiatry* **115**: 1229–241.

Cox, A. and Rutter, M. (1976) Diagnostic Appraisal and Interviewing. In M. Rutter and L. Hersov (eds) *Child Psychiatry – Modern Approaches*. Oxford: Blackwell.

Crisp, A. (1977) Anorexia Nervosa. *Proceedings of The Royal Society of Medicine* **30**: 464.

Crosby, N. (1950) Essential Enuresis. Treatment on Physical Concepts. *Medical Journal of Australia* **2**: 533–43.

Crowe, M. (1973) Conjoint Marital Therapy, Advice or Interpretation. *Journal of Psychosomatic Research* **17**: 309–15.

D'Amato, G. (1969) *Residential Treatment for Child Mental Health.* Springfield, Illinois: Charles C. Thomas.

Dare, C. (1979) Psychoanalysis and Systems in Family Therapy. *Journal of Family Therapy* **I(2)**: 137–51.

Dare, C. and Lindsey, C. (1979) Children in Family Therapy. *Journal of Family Therapy* **I(3)**: 253–70.

De Leon, J. and Mandell, W. (1966) A Comparison of Conditioning and Psychotherapy in the Treatment of Functional Enuresis. *Journal of Clinical Psychology* **22**: 326–30.

Devlin, M. (1962) *Criteria for the Differential Use of Treatment Setting for Children with Emotional Disorders.* New York: Child Welfare League of America.

Dicks, H. (1967) *Marital Tensions.* London: Tavistock.

Dische, S. (1971) Management of Enuresis. *British Medical Journal* **2**: 33–6.

Doane, J. (1978) Family Interaction and Communication Deviance in Disturbed and Normal Families. *Family Process* **17**: 357–76.

Douglas, J. (1979) Behavioural Work with Families. *Journal of Family Therapy* **I(4)**: 371–81.

Douglas, J. W. B. (1975) Early Hospital Admission and Later Disturbance of Behaviour and Learning. *Developmental Medicine and Child Neurology* **17**: 456.

Dubowitz, V. and Hersov, L. (1976) Management of Children with Hysterical Disorders of Motor Function. *Developmental Medicine and Child Neurology* **18**: 358–68.

Eisenson, J. (1971) Speech Defects: Nature, Causes and Psychological Concomitants. In W. Cruikshank, (ed) *Psychology of Exceptional Children and Youth* (3rd ed.) New Jersey: Prentice Hall.

Ellis, M. (1979) Delinquent Drug-takers – A Follow-up. *Journal of Adolescence.* **2**: 17–26.

Eysenck, H. (1967) *The Biological Basis of Personality.* Springfield, Illinois: Charles C. Thomas.

Eysenck, H. and Rachman, S. (1965) *The Causes and Cures of Neurosis.* London: Routledge and Kegan Paul.

Family Welfare Association. *Guide to the Social Services 1980.* London.

Fischer, J. (1976) *The Effectiveness of Social Casework*. Springfield, Illinois: Charles C. Thomas.

Fixson, D., Phillips, E., and Wolf, M. (1973) Achievement Place: Experiments in Self-Government with Pre-Delinquents. *Journal of Applied Behavioural Analysis* **6**: 31–47.

Fraiberg, S. (1959) *The Magic Years*. London: Methuen.

Framo, J. (1970) Symptoms from a Family Transactional Viewpoint. In N. Ackerman, J. Lieb and J. Pierce (eds) *Family Therapy in Transition*. Boston: Little, Brown & Co.

Frank, M. and Zilbach, J. (1968) Current Trends in Group Therapy with Children. *International Journal of Group Psychotherapy* **18**: 447–59.

Freeman, H. and Kendrick, D. (1964) Case of Cat Phobia: Treatment by a Method Derived from Experimental Psychology. In H. Eysenck (ed) *Experiments in Behaviour Therapy*. New York: MacMillan.

Fried, M. (1963) Grieving for a Lost Home. In L. Duhl (ed) *The Urban Condition*. New York: Basic Books.

Fritz, G. (1980) Attempted Suicide in a Five Year-Old Boy. *Clinical Paediatrics* **19(7)**: 448–50.

Frommer, E. (1972) *Diagnosis and Treatment in Clinical Child Psychiatry*. London: Heinemann.

Frude, N. (1980) Methodological Problems in the Evaluation of Family Therapy. *Journal of Family Therapy* **2(1)**: 29–44.

Furth, H. (1969) *Piaget and Knowledge, Theoretical Foundations*. New York: Prentice-Hall.

Gelles, R. (1973) Child Abuse and Psychopathology – A Sociological Critique and Reformulation. *American Journal of Orthopsychiatry* **43(4)**: 611–21.

Gesell, A. (1954) The Autogenesis of Infant Behavior. In L. Carmichael (ed) *Manual of Child Psychology*. New York: Wiley.

Gibbons, J., Bow, I., Butler, J., and Ross, J. (1979) Client's Reactions to Task-centred Casework – A Follow-up Study. *British Journal of Social Work* **9:2**: 203–16.

Ginott, H. (1971) *Group Psychotherapy with Children*. New York: McGraw Hill.

Glick, I. and Kessler, D. (1974) *Marital and Family Therapy*. New York: Grune and Stratton.

Gold, J. and Reisman, J. (1970) An Outcome Study of a Day Treatment Unit School in a Community Mental Health Center. *American Journal of Orthopsychiatry* **40**: 286–87.

Goldberg, E. (1973) Services for the Family. In J. Wing and H. Hafner (eds) *Roots of Evaluation: The Epidemiological Basis for Planning Psychiatric Services*. London: Oxford University Press.

Goldberg, E. and Neill, J. (1972) *Social Work in General Practice*. London: George Allen and Unwin.

Goldberg, E., Warburton, R., Lyons, L., and Willmott, R. (1978) Towards Accountability in Social Work. *British Journal of Social Work* **8**: 3.

Goldstein, H. (1975) A Unitary Approach: Its Rationale and Structure. In F. Ainsworth and J. Hunter (eds) *A Unitary Approach to Social Work Practice – Implications for Education and Organisation*. Dundee: University of Dundee School of Social Administration.

Goodstein, F. (1958) Functional Speech Disorder and Personality. *Journal of Speech Research* **1**: 359.

Gore, E. (1976) *Child Psychiatry Observed*. Oxford: Pergamon.

Gorell Barnes, G. (1973) Working with the Family Group. *Social Work Today* **4**: 3.

—— (1975a) Deprived Adolescents: A Use for Groupwork. *British Journal of Social Work* **5**.

—— (1975b) Seen But Not Heard. Three articles in *Social Work Today* **5**. 20: 606–09; 21: 646–48; 22: 689–93.

Graham, P. (1973) Depression in Pre-pubertal Children. *Developmental Medicine and Child Neurology* **16**: 340–49.

—— (1974) Child Psychiatry and Psychotherapy. *Journal of Child Psychology and Psychiatry* **15(1)**: 59–66.

—— (1977) Environmental Influences on Psycho-social Development. *International Journal of Mental Health* **6(3)**: 7–31.

Graham, P. and Rutter, M. (1973) Psychiatric Disorder in the Young Adolescent: A Follow-up Study. *Proceedings of The Royal Society of Medicine* **66**: 1226–229.

Graham, P., Rutter, M., and George, S. (1973) Temperamental Characteristics as Predictors of Behaviour Disorders in Children. *American Journal of Orthopsychiatry* **43**: 328–39.

Green, A., Gaines, W., and Sandgrund, A. (1974) Child Abuse: Pathological Syndrome of Family Interaction. *American Journal of Psychiatry* **131(8)**: 882–86.

Group for the Advancement of Psychiatry (1970) The Field of Family Therapy. Report No. 78. New York.

Gurman, A. and Kniskern, D. (1979) Research on Marital and Family Therapy: Progress, Perspective and Prospect. In S. Garfield and A. Bergin (eds) *Handbook of Psychotherapy and Behavior Change* (2nd Ed). New York: Wiley.

Haley, J. (1976) *Problem-solving Therapy*. San Francisco: Jossey-Bass.

Hamme, L., Csanyi, A., Gonzales, M., and Rechs, J. (1970) *How to Use Contingency Contracting in the Classroom*. Campaign. Illinois: Research Press.

Harwin, B., Cooper, B., Eastwood, M., and Goldberg, D. (1970) Prospects for Social Work in General Practice. *The Lancet* **2**: 559.

Hazel, N. (1977) How Family Placements Can Combat Delinquency. *Social Work Today* **8**: 6–7.

Hersov, L. (1976) Emotional Disorders. In M. Rutter and L. Hersov (eds) *Child Psychiatry*. Oxford: Blackwell.

Hersov, L. and Bentovim, A. (1976) In-patient Units and Day Hospitals. In M. Rutter and L. Hersov *Child Psychiatry: Modern Approaches*. Oxford: Blackwell.

Hickin, S. (1971) Group Therapy with Deprived Children in a Children's Home in Groups. *Annual Review of the Child Care Association* **28**: 16.

Hill, P. (1979) Child Psychiatry. In P. Hill, R. Murray, and A. Thorley (eds) *Essentials of Postgraduate Psychiatry*. London: Academic Press.

Hollis, F. (1964) *Casework: A Psychosocial Therapy*. New York: Random House.

Howlin, P., Marchant, R., Rutter, M., Berger, M., Hersov, L., and Yule, W. (1973) A Home-based Approach to the Treatment of Autistic Children. *Journal of Autism and Childhood Schizophrenia* **3**: 308–36.

Huntington, J. (1976) Social Work and General Practice: A Review Article. *The Medical Journal of Australia* **I**: 661–63.

Illingworth, R. (1979) *The Normal Child* (7th Ed). London: Churchill Livingstone.

Jackson, D. (1968) (ed) *Human Communication: Volumes I and II*. New York: Science and Behavior Books.

Jackson, B. and Jackson, S. (1979) *Childminder. A Study in Action Research.* London: Routledge and Kegan Paul.

Jehu, D., Hardiker, P., Yelloly, M., and Shaw, M. (1972) *Behaviour Modification in Social Work.* London: John Wiley & Sons.

Jenkins, S. (1969) Separation Experiences of Parents whose Children are in Foster Care. *Child Welfare* (Vol. XVIII) **6**: 334–41.

Jephcott, P. (1971) *Homes in High Flats; Some of the Human Problems Involved in Multi-storey Housing.* Edinburgh: Oliver and Boyd.

Johnson, C. and Katz, R. (1973) Using Parents as Change Agents for their Children – A Review. *Journal of Child Psychology and Psychiatry* **14**: 181–200.

Johnson, W. (1959) *The Onset of Stuttering.* London: Oxford University Press.

Joselyn, I. (1972) Adolescent Group Therapy: Why, When and a Caution. In I. Berkowitz (ed) *Adolescents Grow in Groups.* London: Butterworths.

Kadushin, A. (1977) *Consultation in Social Work.* New York: Columbia University Press.

Kanner, L. (1943) Autistic Disturbances of Affective Contact. *Nervous Children* **2**: 217–50.

—— (1959) Trends in Child Psychiatry. *Journal of Mental Science* **105**: 581–93.

Karn, E. (1972) Residential Group Project for Mothers of Children Referred to a Child Guidance Clinic. *British Journal of Social Work* **2**: 175–86.

Kellmer Pringle, M. (1974a) Identifying Deprived Children. *Proceedings of The Royal Society of Medicine* **67**: 39–40.

—— (1974b) *The Needs of Children.* London: Hutchinson.

Kelly, G. (1955) *The Psychology of Personal Constructs.* New York: Norton.

Kempe, C. and Helfer, R. (1968) *The Battered Child.* Chicago: University of Chicago Press.

Kennedy, W. (1971) A Behaviouristic, Community-oriented Approach to School Phobia and Other Disorders. In H. Richard (ed) *Behavioural Intervention in Human Problems.* Oxford: Pergamon.

Kenyon, F. (1970) Homosexuality in the Female. *British Journal of Hospital Medicine.* February: 183.

King, R., Raynes, N., and Tizard, J. (1971) *Patterns of Residential Care.*

London: Routledge and Kegan Paul.

Kolvin, I., Taunch, J., Currah, J., Garside, R., Nolan, J., and Shaw, W. (1972) Enuresis: A Descriptive Analysis and Controlled Trial. *Developmental Medicine and Child Neurology* **14**: 715–26.

Kolvin, I., MacKeith, R., and Meadow, S. (1973) Bladder Control and Enuresis. *Clinics in Developmental Medicine*. 48 and 49. London: Heinemann.

Kondas, O. (1967) Reduction of Exam Anxiety and Stage Fright by Group Desensitisation and Relaxing. *Behavioural Research and Therapy* **5**: 275–81.

Kufeld, K. (1979) Temporary Foster Care. *British Journal of Social Work*. **9(1)**: 49–66.

Kushner, M. (1965) Desensitisation of a Post-Traumatic Phobia. In L. Ullman and L. Krasner (eds) *Case Studies in Behaviour Modification*. New York: Holt, Rinehart, and Winston.

Lask, B. (1980) Evaluation, Why and How – A Guide for Clinicians. *Journal of Family Therapy* **2(2)**: 199–210.

—— (1981) Illness in the Family – A Conceptual Model. In S. Walrond Skinner *Family Therapy*. *Recent Developments*. London: Routledge and Kegan Paul.

Laslett, R. (1977) *Educating Maladjusted Children*. London: Crosby, Lockwood and Staples.

Laufer, M., Laffey, J., and Davidson, R. (1974) Residential Treatment for Children and its Derivatives. In G. Caplan (ed) *American Handbook of Psychiatry*. *Volume II* (2nd Ed). New York: Basic Books.

Lazarus, A. (1960) The Elimination of Children's Phobias by Deconditioning. In H. Eysenck (ed) *Behaviour Therapy and Neurosis*. Oxford: Pergamon.

—— (1966) Behavioural Rehearsal versus Non-directive Therapy versus Advice in Effecting Behavioural Change. *Behaviour Research and Therapy* **4(3)**: 209–12.

Lazarus, A. and Abramovitz, A. (1962) The Use of 'Emotive Imagery' in the Treatment of Children's Phobias. *Journal of Mental Science* **108**: 191–95.

Lazarus, A., Davison, G., and Polefka, D. (1965) Classical and Operant Factors in the Treatment of School Phobia. *Journal of Abnormal Psychology* **70**: 225–29.

Leach, P. (1974) *Babyhood: Infant Development, 0–2*. London: Penguin.

Leichter, E. and Schulman, G. (1974) Multi-Family Group Therapy. *Family Process* **13:1**: 95–109.

Leigh, D., Pare, C., and Marks, J. (1972) (eds) *Encyclopaedia of Psychiatry for General Practitioners*. Roche Products Limited.

Levere, R. and Kirk, M. (1979) A Combined Therapeutic Approach in a Family Setting. *Journal of Family Therapy* **I(3)**: 271–80.

Levy, D. (1943) *Maternal Overprotection*. New York: Columbia University Press.

Liberman, R. (1970) Behavioural Approaches to Family and Couple Therapy. *American Journal of Orthopsychiatry* **40**: 106–18.

Lidz, T. (1968) Family Organisation and Personality Structure. In N. Bell and E. Vogel (eds) *A Modern Introduction to the Family*. New York: Free Press.

Lieberman, S. (1980) *Transgenerational Family Therapy*. London: Croom Helm.

Liederman, P., Tulkin, S., and Rosenfeld, A. (1977) *Culture and Infancy*. New York: Academic Press.

Lindsey, C. (1979) Working with Rage and Anger – The Establishment of a Therapeutic Setting in the Homes of Multi-problem Families. *Journal of Family Therapy* **I(2):** 117–24.

Lloyd-Davies, A. (1960) As Others See Us. In *Ventures in Professional Co-operation: Mental Health in Clinic, Hospital and Community*. Published by Association of Psychiatric Social Workers.

Lynch, M. (1975) Ill-health and Child Abuse. *Lancet* **II**: 317–19.

McAuley, R. and McAuley, P. (1977) *Child Behaviour Problems – An Empirical Approach to Management*. London: Macmillan.

Maclennan, B. and Felsonfeldt, N. (1968) *Group Counseling and Psychotherapy with Adolescents*. New York: Columbia University Press.

Madanes, C. and Haley, J. (1977) Dimensions of Family Therapy *Journal of Nervous and Mental Diseases* **165(2)**: 88–98.

Magrab, P. (1978) *Psychological Management of Paediatric Problems*. Vol. 1. Baltimore: University Park Press.

Marks, I. (1969) *Fears and Phobias*. London: Heinemann.

—— (1974) Research in Neurosis: A Selective Review. II Treatment. *Psychological Medicine* **4**: 89–109.

Martin, F. (1977) Some Implications from the Theory and Practice of Family Therapy for Individual Therapy (and vice versa). *British Journal of Medical Psychology* **50**: 53–63.

Masterton, G. (1979) The Management of Solvent-abuse. *Journal of Adolescence* **2**: 65–75.

Mayer, J. and Timms, N. (1970) *The Client Speaks: Working-class Impressions of Casework*. London: Routledge and Kegan Paul.

Meyer, V. and Chesser, E. (1970) *Behaviour Therapy in Clinical Psychiatry*. Harmondsworth: Penguin.

Mills, G. (1979) Family Therapy Involving Several Agencies *Social Work Today* **10(32)**: 18–20.

Minde, K. and Cohen, N. (1979) Cross-cultural Approach to Child Psychiatry as Applied to the Infant and Young Child. In J. Howells (ed) *Modern Perspectives in the Psychiatry of Infancy*. New York: Brunner/Mazel.

Minton, C., Kagan, J., and Levine, J. (1971) Maternal Control and Obedience in the Two year-old Child. *Child Development* **42**: 1873–894.

Minuchin, S. (1974) *Families and Family Therapy*. London: Tavistock.

Minuchin, S., Montalvo, B., Guerney, B., Rosman, B., and Shumer, F. (1967) *Families of the Slums: An Exploration of their Structure and Treatment*. New York: Basic Books.

Minuchin, S., Rosman, B., and Baker, L. (1978) *Psychosomatic Families*. Cambridge: Harvard Press.

Mitchell, R. E. (1971) Some Social Implications of High-density Housing. *American Social Review* **36**: 18–29.

Montenegro, H. (1968) Severe Separation Anxiety in Two Pre-school Children Successfully Treated by Reciprocal Inhibition. *Journal of Child Psychology and Psychiatry* **9**: 93–103.

Moore, E. (1961) School Visits: The Role of Phantasy. *Journal of Child Psychology and Psychiatry* **2(2)**: 127–35.

Moore, N. (1974) Psychiatric Illness and Living in Flats. *British Journal of Psychiatry* **125**: 500–07.

Morgan, R. and Young, G. (1972) The Conditioning Treatment of Childhood Enuresis. *British Journal of Social Work* **3:4**: 503–09.

Mostow, E. and Newberry, P. (1975) Work Role and Depression in Women. *American Journal of Orthopsychiatry* **45**: 538.

Mrazak, P. (1980) Sexual Abuse of Children. *Journal of Child Psychology and Psychiatry* **21(1)**: 91–6.

Nakhla, F., Folkart, L., and Webster, J. (1969) Treatment of Families as In-patients. *Family Process* **8**: 79–96.

Newson, J. and Newson, E. (1976) *Seven year-olds in the Home Environment*. London: Allen and Unwin.

Nurse, J. (1972) Retarded Infants and their Parents – A Group for Fathers and Mothers. *British Journal of Social Work* **2(2)**: 159–76.

Obler, M. and Terwilliger, R. (1970) Pilot Study of the Effectiveness of Systematic Desensitisation with Neurologically Impaired Children with Phobic Disorders. *Journal of Consultative and Clinical Psychology* **34**: 314–18.

Oliver, J. and Buchanan, H. (1979) Generations of Maltreated Children and Multi-agency Care in One Kindred. *British Journal of Psychiatry* **135**: 289–303.

Olson, U. and Pegg, P. (1979) Direct Open Supervision: A Team Approach. *Family Process* **18**: 463–69.

Papp, P. (1980) The Greek Chorus and Other Techniques of Family Therapy. *Family Process* **19(1)**: 45–57.

Parad, H. (1965) *Crisis Intervention: Selected Readings*. Family Service Association of America.

Patterson, G. (1971) *Families: Applications of Social Learning to Family Life*. Illinois: Research Press.

—— (1973a) Reprograming of the Families of Aggressive Boys. In C. E. Thoresen (ed) *Behavior Modification in Education*. Chicago: National Society for the Study of Education.

—— (1973b) Multiple Evaluations of a Parent-Training Program. In T. Thompson and W. Dockens (eds) *Proceedings of the International Symposium in Behavior Modification*. New York: Appleton-Century-Crofts.

Paul, N. (1967) The Role of Mourning and Empathy in Conjoint Marital Therapy. In G. Zuk and I. Boszormenyi-Nagy (eds) *Family Therapy and Disturbed Families*. Palo Alto: Science and Behavior Books.

Pease, J. (1979) A Social Skills Training Group for Early Adolescents. *Journal of Adolescence* **2**: 229–38.

Perlman, H. (1971) *Perspectives on Social Casework*. Philadelphia: Temple University Press.

Pilling, D. and Kellmer Pringle, M. (1978) *Controversial Issues in Child Development*. Elek Publications.

Pincus, A. and Minahan, A. (1973) *Social Work Practice – Model and Method*. Itason, Illinois: Peacock.

Pollak, M. (1979) Housing and Mothering – Their Effects upon the Developmental Levels of Three year-old Children. *Archives of Diseases in Childhood* **54**: 54–8.

Power, M., Benn, R., and Morris, J. (1972) Neighbourhood, School and Juveniles before the Courts. *British Journal of Criminology* **12**: 111–32.

Rapoport, L. (1970) Crisis Intervention as a Mode of Brief Treatment. In R. Roberts and R. Nee (eds) *Theories of Social Casework*. Chicago: University of Chicago Press.

Reavley, W. and Gilbert, T. (1979) The Behavioural Treatment Approach to Potential Child Abuse. *Social Work Today* **7:6**: 166–68.

Reed, G. (1963) Elective Mutism in Children – A Re-appraisal. *Journal of Child Psychology and Psychiatry* **4**: 99–107.

Reid, W. and Epstein, L. (1972) *Task Centered Casework*. New York: Columbia University Press.

Reid, W. and Shyne, A. (1969) *Brief and Extended Casework*. New York: Columbia University Press.

Richman, N. (1974) The Effects of Housing on Pre-school Children and their Mothers. *Developmental Medicine and Clinical Neurology* **16**: 53–8.

Richman, N. (1977) Behaviour Problems in Three Year-old Children: Family and Social Factors. *British Journal of Psychiatry* **131**: 523–27.

Rivinus, T., Jannison, D., and Graham, P. (1975) Childhood Organic Neurological Disease Presenting as Psychiatric Disorder. *Archives of Diseases in Childhood* **50**: 115–19.

Roberts, R. and Nee, R. (1970) (eds) *Theories of Social Casework*. Chicago: University of Chicago Press.

Robins, L. (1966) *Deviant Children Grown Up*. Baltimore: Williams and Wilkins.

Robins, L. (1973) Evaluation of Psychiatric Services in the United States. In J. Wing and H. Hafner (eds) *Roots of Evaluation: The Epidemiological Basis for Planning Psychiatric Services*. London: Oxford University Press.

Robinson, R. and Henry, S. (1977) *Self-help and Health*. London: Martin Robertson.

Rogers, D., Tripp, J., Bentovim, A., Robinson, A., Berry, D., and

Goulding, R. (1976) Non-accidental Poisoning: An Extended Syndrome of Child Abuse. *British Medical Journal* **1**: 793–96.

Rose, G. and Marshall, T. (1974) *Counselling and School Social Work.* London: John Wiley.

Rose, S. (1975) *Treating Children in Groups.* San Francisco: Jossey-Bass.

Ross, A. (1972) Behavior Therapy. In B. Welman (ed) *Manual of Child Psychopathology.* New York: McGraw Hill.

—— (1974) *Psychological Disorders of Children.* New York: McGraw Hill.

Russell, P. (1976) *Help Starts Here.* London: National Children's Bureau.

Rutter, M. (1967) A Children's Behaviour Questionnaire for Completion by Teachers. *Journal of Child Psychology and Psychiatry* **8**: 1-11.

—— (1971) Normal Psycho-sexual Development. *Journal of Child Psychology and Psychiatry* **11**: 259–83.

—— (1972) *Maternal Deprivation Reassessed.* Harmondsworth: Penguin.

—— (1974) The Development of Infantile Autism. *Psychological Medicine* **4**: 147–63.

—— (1975) *Helping Troubled Children.* Harmondsworth: Penguin.

—— (1976) Separation, Loss and Family Relationships. In M. Rutter and L. Hersov (eds) *Child Psychiatry.* Oxford: Blackwell.

Rutter, M. and Bartak, L. (1973) Special Education Treatment of Autistic Children – A Comparative Study. *Journal of Child Psychology and Psychiatry.* **14**: 241–70.

Rutter, M., Cox, A., Tupling, C., Berger, M., and Yule, W. (1975) Attainment and Adjustment in Two Geographical Areas. *British Journal of Psychiatry* **126**: 493–509.

Rutter, M. and Madge, N. (1976) *Cycles of Disadvantage.* London: Heinemann Educational.

Rutter, M. and Martin, J. (1972) The Child with Delayed Speech. *Clinics in Developmental Medicine, No. 43.* London: SIMP/Heinemann.

Rutter, M., Maugham, B., Mortimore, P., and Ouston, J. (1979) *15,000 Hours.* London: Open Books.

Rutter, M., Shaffer, D. and Sturge, C. (1975) *A Multi-axial Classification of Child Psychiatric Disorders.* Geneva: World Health Organisation.

Rutter, M. and Sussenwein, F. (1971) A Developmental and Behavioural Approach to the Treatment of Pre-school Autistic Children. *Journal of Autism and Child Schizophrenia* **I**: 376–97.

Rutter, M., Tizard, J., and Whitmore, K. (1970) *Education, Health and Behaviour*. London: Longman.

Rutter, M., Tizard, J., Yule, W., Graham, P., and Whitmore, K. (1976) Research Report, Isle of Wight Studies. *Psychological Medicine* **6**: 313–32.

Rutter, M., Yule, W., Berger, M., Yule, B., Morton, J., and Bagley, C. (1974) Children of West Indian Immigrants. *Journal of Child Psychology and Psychiatry*. **15**: 241.

Rycroft, C. (1968) *A Critical Dictionary of Psychoanalysis*. London: Nelson.

Safer, D. and Allen, R. (1976) *Hyperactive Children: Diagnosis and Management*. Baltimore: University Park Press.

Satir, V. (1978) *Conjoint Family Therapy*. London: Souvenir Press.

Schmitt, B. (1975) The Minimal Brain Dysfunction Myth. *American Journal of Diseases of Children* **129**: 1313–319.

Scott, D., Kolvin, I., Tweddle, E., and McLaren, M. (1976) Psychiatric Care of Children and Adolescents. In A. Baker (ed) *Comprehensive Psychiatric Care*. Oxford: Blackwell.

Scott, P. (1965) Delinquency. In J. Howells (ed) *Modern Perspectives in Child Psychiatry*. Edinburgh: Oliver and Boyd.

—— (1977) Non-accidental Injury in Children. *British Journal of Psychiatry* **131**: 366–80.

Selvini Palazzoli, M., Boscolo, L., Cecchin, G., and Prata, G. (1978) *Paradox and Counter-paradox*. New York: Aronson.

Shaffer, D. (1974) Suicide in Childhood and Early Adolescence. *Journal of Child Psychology and Psychiatry* **15**: 275–92.

Shields, J. (1973) Heredity and Psychological Abnormality. In H. Eysenck (ed) *Handbook of Abnormal Psychology*. London: Pitman Medical.

Skynner, R. (1976) *One Flesh: Separate Persons*. London: Constable.

—— (1979) Family Therapist as Family Scapegoat. *Journal of Family Therapy* **I(1)**: 7–22.

Slavson, S. (1955) Group Psychotherapies. In J. McCary (ed) *Six Approaches to Psychotherapy*. New York: Dryden Press.

Sluckin, A. (1975) Encopresis – A Behavioural Approach Described. *Social Work Today* **5**: 643–46.

Smirnoff, V. (1971) *The Scope of Child Analysis*. London: Routledge and Kegan Paul.

Solomon, M. (1969) Family Therapy Dropouts: Resistance to Change. *Canadian Psychiatric Association Journal* **14**: 21–9.

Speight, A., Bridson, J., and Cooper, C. (1979) Follow-Up Survey of Cases of Child Abuse. *Child Abuse and Neglect* **3**: 555–63.

Steinberg, D. (1976) Psychotic Disorders in Adolescence. In M. Rutter and L. Hersov (eds) *Child Psychiatry*. Oxford: Blackwell.

Steirlin, H. (1972) *Separating Parents and Adolescents*. New York: Quadrangle.

Stewart, M. and Olds, S. (1973) *Raising a Hyperactive Child*. London: Harper Row.

Stott, D. (1973) Follow-up Study From Birth of the Effects of Prenatal Stress. *Developmental Medicine and Child Neurology* **15**: 770–87.

Stuart, R. (1967) Applications of Behaviour Theory to Social Casework. In Edwin J. Thomas (ed) *The Socio-behavioural Approach and Applications to Social Work*. New York: Council on Social Work Education.

Sturton, S. (1972) Developing Groupwork in a Casework Agency. *British Journal of Social Work* **2(2)**: 143–58.

Sussenwein, F. (1976) Psychiatric Social Work. In M. Rutter and L. Hersov (eds) *Child Psychiatry – Modern Approaches*. Oxford: Blackwell.

Sutton, C. (1979) *Psychology for Social Workers and Counsellors*. London: Routledge and Kegan Paul.

Tharp, R. and Wetzel, R. (1969) *Behaviour Modification in the Natural Environment*. London: Academic Press.

Thomas, A. and Chess, S. (1977) *Temperament and Development*. New York: Brunner/Mazel Publishers.

Thomas, A., Chess, S., and Birch, H. (1968) *Temperament and Behavior Disorders in Children*. New York: University Press.

Thompson, L. (1973) Learning Disabilities – An Overview. *American Journal of Psychiatry* **130**: 393–99.

Thompson, S. and Kahn, J. (1970) *The Group Process as a Helping Technique*. London: Pergamon.

Tizard, B. and Rees, J. (1975) The Effects of Early Institutional Rearing. *Journal of Child Psychology and Psychiatry* **16**: 61–74.

Tolstrup, K. (1975) Treatment of Anorexia Nervosa in Children. *Journal of Child Psychology and Psychiatry* **16**: 75–8.

Truax, C. (1966) Reinforcement and Non-reinforcement in Rogerian Psychotherapy. *Journal of Abnormal Psychology.* **71(1)**: 1–9.

Turner, R. (1973) Conditioning Treatment of Nocturnal Enuresis: Present Status. In I. Kolvin, R. Mackeith, and S. Meadow (eds) *Bladder Control and Enuresis.* Clinics in Developmental Medicine, Numbers 48/49. London: SIMP/Heinemann.

Tyrer, P. and Tyrer, S. (1974) School Refusal, Truancy and Neurotic Illness. *Psychological Medicine* **4**: 416–21.

Waldfogel, S., Coolidge, J., and Hahn, P. (1957) The Development, Meaning and Management of School Phobia. *American Journal of Orthopsychiatry* **27**: 754–76.

Walrond-Skinner, S. (1976) *Family Therapy – The Treatment of Natural Systems.* London: Routledge and Kegan Paul.

—— (1978) Indications and Contraindications for the Use of Family Therapy. *Journal of Child Psychology and Psychiatry* **19**: 57–62.

Wardle, C. (1974) Residential Care of Children with Conduct Disorders. In P. Barker (ed) *Residential Psychiatric Treatment of Children.* London: Crosby, Lockwood and Staples.

Warren, W. (1968) A study of anorexia nervosa in young girls. *Journal of Child Psychology and Psychiatry* **9**: 27–40.

Waterhouse, J. (1978) Groupwork in Intermediate Treatment. *British Journal of Social Work* **8(2)**: 127–44.

Watson, J. and Rayner, R. (1920) Conditioned Emotional Reactions. *Journal of Experimental Psychology.* **3**: 1–14.

Watzlawick, P. and Weakland, J. (1977) (eds) *The Interactional View.* New York: Norton Press.

Watzlawick, P., Weakland, J., and Fisch, R. (1974) *Change.* New York: Norton Press.

Weller, S. (1975) The Patient is the Family. *World Medicine*, November 19. 36–8.

Wessel, M. (1978) The Grieving Child. *Clinical Paediatrics* **17(7)**: 559–68.

West, D. (1974) *Who Becomes Delinquent?* London: Heinemann.

—— (1976) Delinquency. In M. Rutter and L. Hersov (eds) *Child Psychiatry.* Oxford: Blackwell.

West, D. and Farrington, D. (1973) *Who Becomes Delinquent?* London: Heinemann Educational.

Wilson, L. (1976) The Social Worker in General Practice. *The Medical Journal of Australia* **1**: 664–66.

Winefield, H. and Peay, N. (1980) *Behavioural Science in Medicine.* London: George Allen and Unwin.

Wing, L. (1976) (ed) *Early Childhood Autism: Clinical, Educational and Social Aspects* (2nd Ed). Oxford: Pergamon.

Wingate, M. (1976) *Stuttering: Theory and Treatment.* New York: Irvington.

Winnicott, C. (1968) Face to Face with Children. In *Child Care and Social Work.* London: Bookstall.

Winnicott, D. (1971a) *Therapeutic Consultations in Child Psychiatry.* London: Hogarth Press and The Institute of Psychoanalysis.

—— (1971b) *Playing and Reality.* London: Tavistock.

Wolfensberger, W. (1968) Counselling the Parents of the Retarded. In A. Baumeister (ed) *Mental Retardation: Appraisal, Education and Rehabiliation.* London: University of London Press.

Wolff, S. (1974) The Fate of the Adopted Child. *Archives of Diseases in Childhood* **49**: 165–70.

Wolkind, S. (1974a) The Components of Affectionless Psychopathy in Institutionalised Children. *Journal of Child Psychology and Psychiatry* **15(3)**: 215–20.

—— (1974b) Sex Differences in the Aetiology of Anti-social Disorder in Children. *British Journal of Psychiatry* **125**: 125–30.

—— (1977) Women Who Have Been In Care – Psychological and Social Status During Pregnancy. *Journal of Child Psychology* **18:2**: 179–82.

—— (1978) Fostering the Disturbed Child – Annotation. *Journal of Child Psychology and Psychiatry* **19(4)**: 393–97.

Wolkind, S. and Rutter, M. (1973) Children Who Have Been In Care. *Journal of Child Psychology and Psychiatry* **14**: 97–105.

Name index

Abramowitz, A. 146, 190
Ackerman, N. 95, 99, 181
Adcock, M. 159, 181
Aitken, P. 22, 181
Alexander, J. 67, 98, 181
Andolfi, M. 99, 104, 107, 109, 181
Anthony, E. 25, 135, 181
Apley, J. 158, 181
Atkins, T. 169, 181

Baird, P. 8, 182
Baker, H. 58, 182
Baker, L. 82–5, 107, 192
Bancroft, J. 87, 182
Bandura, A. 139–40, 142, 182
Bannister, D. 51, 182
Barker, P. 9, 167–8, 182
Barnes, G. 96, 182
Barnes, J. 21, 182
Bartak, L. 68, 195
Bateson, G. 69, 97, 182
Becker, W. 67, 182
Beels, C. 99, 182
Benn, R. 65, 194
Bentovim, A. 72, 95, 99, 109, 182, 188
Berger, M. 64, 91, 183
Berkowitz, J. 135, 183
Bernal, J. 69, 183
Berry, J. 124–5, 183
Bingley, E. 72, 158, 183
Black, D. 15, 183
Blinder, B. 84, 183
Blurton-Jones, N. 69, 183

Boszormenyi-Nagy, I. 99, 183
Bowen, M. 95, 99, 183
Bowlby, J. 11, 13, 183
Bridson, J. 89, 197
Brophy, J. 22, 183
Bruch, H. 83–4, 183
Buchanan, H. 19, 193
Byng-Hall, J. 95–6, 184

Caplan, G. 8, 155, 184
Caplan, H. 61, 184
Carr, A. 60, 184
Carr, J. 117, 184
Chess, S. 24–5, 156, 184, 197
Chesser, E. 60, 192
Churven, P. 38, 184
Cohen, N. 11, 192
Coleman, J. 22, 184
Coolidge, J. 58, 198
Cooper, C. 89, 197
Cox, A. 29, 184
Crisp, A. 83, 85, 184
Crosby, N. 143, 184
Crowe, M. 98, 184

D'Amato, G. 169, 185
Dare, C. 32, 38, 95, 99, 185
Davidson, R. 168, 190
Davison, G. 141, 190
De Leon, J. 143, 185
Devlin, M. 169, 185
Dicks, H. 99, 185
Doane, J. 64, 185

Douglas, J. 98, 185
Douglas, J. W. B. 13, 185
Dubowitz, V. 62, 185

Eisenson, J. 80, 185
Ellis, M. 86, 185
Eysenck, H. 140, 149, 185

Farrington, D. 64, 199
Ferber, A. 99, 182
Fischer, J. 8, 186
Fixson, D. 151, 186
Folkart, L. 168, 192
Framo, J. 96, 186
Frank, M. 134, 186
Fransella, F. 51, 182
Freeman, D. 84, 183
Freeman, H. 141, 186
Freud, A. 127
Fried, M. 164, 186
Fritz, G. 59, 186
Frommer, E. 59, 174, 186
Frude, N. 7, 186
Furth, H. 11, 186

Gaines, W. 88, 187
Gelles, R. 88, 186
George, S. 25, 66, 185
Gesell, A. 11, 186
Gibbons, J. 119, 186
Gilbert, T. 90, 194
Ginott, H. 132-3, 136, 186
Glick, I. 109, 186
Gold, J. 169, 187
Goldberg, E. 8, 118-19, 157, 187
Goldstein, H. 118, 187
Good, T. 22, 183
Goodstein, F. 80, 187
Gore, E. 83, 187
Gorell Barnes, G. 132, 136-7, 156, 187
Graham, P. 18, 20, 25, 60, 66-7, 129, 187, 194
Green, A. 88, 187
Gurman, A. 37, 95, 188

Hahn, P. 58, 198
Haley, J. 97-9, 109, 188, 191
Hamme, L. 151, 188
Harwin, B. 157, 188
Hassibi, A. 156, 184
Helfer, R. 151, 189
Henry, S. 165, 194

Hersov, L. 56, 58, 62, 167-9, 185
Hickin, S. 137, 188
Hill, P. 54, 63, 188
Howlin, P. 68, 120, 188
Huntington, J. 157, 188

Illingworth, R. 69, 188

Jackson, B. and S. 169, 189
Jackson, D. 97, 188
Jannison, D. 62, 194
Jehu, D. 140, 189
Jenkins, S. 170, 189
Jephcott, P. 164, 189
Johnson, C. 67, 189
Johnson, W. 80, 189
Joselyn, I. 132, 189

Kadushin, A. 155, 189
Kagan, J. 65, 192
Kahn, J. 131, 197
Kanner, L. 3, 189
Kellmer Pringle, M. 17, 25, 189, 193
Kelly, G. 51, 189
Kempe, C. 151, 189
Kendrick, D. 141, 186
Kennedy, W. 139, 147, 189
Kenyon, F. 87, 189
Kessler, D. 109, 186
Klein, M. 127
King, R. 171, 189
Kirk, M. 98, 191
Kniskern, D. 37, 95, 188
Kolvin, I. 139, 190
Kondas, O. 146, 190
Kufeld, K. 170, 190
Kushner, M. 141, 190

Laffey, J. 168, 190
Lask, B. 8, 82, 106, 190
Laslett, R. 164, 190
Laufer, M. 168, 190
Lazarus, A. 135, 141, 146, 190
Leichter, E. 136, 191
Leigh, D. 60, 191
Levere, R. 98, 191
Levine, J. 65, 192
Levy, D. 15, 191
Liberman, R. 98, 191
Lidz, T. 12, 191
Lieberman, S. 96, 98, 191
Liederman, P. 11, 191

Lindsey, C. 32, 36, 38, 185, 191
Lloyd-Davies, A. 160, 191
Lucas, H. 21, 182
Lynch, M. 88, 191

McAuley, R. and P. 141, 152, 191
Madanes, C. 98, 191
Madge, N. 17, 22, 65, 195
Magrab, P. 120, 191
Marks, J. 60, 139, 141, 145, 191
Marshall, T. 119, 125, 197
Martin, F. 109, 191
Masterton, G. 86, 192
Mayer, J. 119, 192
Meyer, V. 60, 192
Mills, G. 4, 112, 155, 159, 192
Minahan, A. 5, 39–40, 131, 138, 194
Minde, K. 11, 192
Minton, C. 65, 192
Minuchin, S. 12, 32, 38, 82–5, 97–9, 107
    110, 192
Mitchell, R. E. 164, 192
Montenegro, H. 146, 192
Moore, E. 156, 192
Moore, N. 20, 192
Morgan, R. 143, 151, 192
Morris, J. 65, 194
Mostow, E. 17, 192
Mrazak, P. 88, 192

Nakhla, F. 168, 192
Neill, J. 157, 187
Newberry, P. 17, 192
Newson, J. and E. 65, 193
Nurse, J. 137, 193

Obler, M. 146, 193
Oliver, J. 19, 193
Olson, U. 111, 193

Papp, P. 111, 193
Pare, C. 60, 191
Parsons, B. 67, 98, 181
Patterson, G. 99, 149–50
Paul, N. 95, 193
Pavlov, I. 140
Pease, J. 135, 193
Pegg, P. 111, 193
Phillips, E. 151, 186
Piaget, J. 1, 11
Pilling, D. 17, 193
Pincus, A. 5, 39–40, 131, 138, 194

Polefka, D. 141, 190
Pollak, M. 20, 194
Power, M. 65, 194

Rachman, S. 149, 185, 194
Rapoport, L. 119, 138, 194
Rayner, R. 140, 198
Raynes, N. 171, 189
Reavley, W. 90, 194
Rees, J. 171, 197
Reid, W. 8, 119, 194
Reisman, J. 169, 187
Richman, N. 14, 20, 194
Rivinus, T. 62, 194
Robins, L. 67, 136, 194
Robinson, R. 165, 194
Rogers, C. 138
Rogers, D. 88, 194
Rose, G. 119, 125, 195
Rose, S. 131, 134, 136, 195
Rosenfeld, A. 11, 191
Rosman, B. 82–5, 107, 192
Ross, A. 140, 147, 195
Russell, P. 55, 195
Rutter, M. 183–4, 187, 195–6, 199; on
    autism 68; on anti-social behaviour
    150; on bonding 9, 12–15; on emotional
    disturbance 24–5, 55, 64–7, 158; on
    family 17–18, 29, 65; on flooding 146;
    on group work 131; on interviewing
    29; on labelling 22; on reading 91; on
    schools 21, 39; on sexual disorders 86;
    on urban life 20
Rycroft, C. 60, 196

Sandgrun, A. 88, 187
Satir, V. 11, 38, 97, 99, 196
Schmitt, B. 79, 196
Schulman, G. 136, 191
Scott, D. 159, 196
Scott, P. 87, 89, 196
Selvini Palazzoli, M. 109, 196
Shaffer, D. 55, 59, 64, 195–6
Shields, J. 22, 196
Shyne, A. 8, 119, 194
Skinner, B. F. 141
Skynner, R. 95, 107, 196
Slavson, S. 133, 196
Smirnoff, V. 11, 127, 197
Solomon, M. 108, 197
Spark, G. 99, 183
Speight, A. 89, 197

Steinberg, D. 69, 197
Stott, D. 23, 197
Stuart, R. 138, 197
Stunkard, A. 84, 183
Sturge, C. 55, 64, 195
Sturton, S. 132–3, 136–7, 197
Sussenwein, F. 3, 68, 94, 117, 156, 195, 197
Sutton, C. 117, 151, 197

Terwilliger, R. 146, 193
Tharp, R. 151, 197
Thomas, A. 24–5, 120, 197
Thompson, S. 131, 197
Timms, N. 119, 192
Tizard, B. 171, 197
Tizard, J. 24, 65–6, 158, 189, 196
Tolstrup, K. 84, 198
Truax, C. 138, 198
Tulkin, S. 11, 191
Turner, R. 143, 198

Waldfogel, S. 58, 198
Walrond-Skinner, S. 5, 6, 29, 94, 96, 109, 198

Walters, R. 142, 182
Wardle, W. 63, 198
Warren, W. 83, 85, 198
Waterhouse, J. 137, 198
Watson, J. 140, 198
Watzlawick, P. 97, 99, 198
Weakland, J. 97, 99, 198
Webster, J. 168, 192
Weller, S. 37, 198
Wessel, M. 15, 198
West, D. 22, 64, 198–9
Wetzel, R. 151, 197
White, R. 159, 181
Whitmore, K. 24, 65–6, 158, 196
Wills, U. 58, 182
Wilson, L. 157, 199
Winnicott, C. 43, 124, 126–7, 199
Wolf, M. 151, 186
Wolfensberger, W. 117, 120, 199
Wolff, S. 18, 199
Wolkind, S. 66, 170–1, 199

Young, G. 143, 151, 192
Yule, W. 64, 91, 183

Zilbach, J. 134, 186

Subject index

abuse, child 87–90, 125–6, 151
Achievement Place 150
activity of therapists 98–9
Acts: Children and Young Persons' *1963*
   165; *1969* 170, 184; Children's *1975*
   159; Education *1944* 3
adaptability 97
adjustment reactions 87
adolescent: behaviour modification 151;
   delinquency 64; depression 59; drug
   abuse 85–6; and family 97–8, 107;
   group therapy with 135–6; peer groups
   21–2
adoption 18–19, 90
Advancement of Psychiatry, Group for
   the 188
AFASIC *see* Association for All Speech
   Impaired Children
aide-memoire: for family assessment 36;
   for family therapy 100; for history
   taking 44; for interviewing child 47
alcohol 22, 85–6
alternative forms of care 167–71
amitryptyline 174
amphetamines 78, 85, 174
analytical theory 60
anorexia nervosa 83–4, 107; *see also*
   feeding problems
ante-natal period *see* pregnancy
anticonvulsants 174
antidepressants 59, 173–4
anti-social behaviour 15, 22, 42–3, 63–7;
   and behaviour modification 148–51;

and family 64–5; and hospitalization
   167–8; in parents 17–18; *see also*
   delinquency
anxiety *see* fears
aphasia 48, 92; *see also* speech problems
assessment *see* child assessment; family
   assessment
Association for All Speech Impaired
   Children 92
Association for Family Therapy 116
asthma 52, 82
atmosphere 32
audiotape 110–11
authority in family therapy 107–8
autism 67–8, 92, 120, 165
avoidance learning 143

background to child psychiatry 1–10
barbiturates 85, 173–4
bed wetting *see* enuresis
behaviour difficulties *see* anti-social
   behaviour
behaviour modification 66, 84, 98, 123,
   138–53
behaviour therapy groups 134–5
behavioural analysis 90
belle indifférence 61
Bene-Anthony test 50–1
bereavement 15, 18, 86, 121; *see also*
   separation
biological factors 22–5
bonding 9, 12–19
Boy Scouts 166

brain: damage 66, 174; dysfunction
23–4, 78–9, 92

Canada 170
carbamazepine 174
case illustrations *see* example cases
casework: adherence to 3; with children
124–6; definition of 117–18, 124;
family 94; individual and counselling
117–30; lack of value 66; with parents
119–20; stages of 120–3; strategies of
123–4
causation of disorders 11–26
change, environmental 162–7
child: abuse 87–90, 125–6, 151;
assessment 40–4; casework with
124–6; development 42–50, 90–3;
disorders of 11–26, 54–93; intelligence
46–8, 65, 77–8, 86, 93, 163; interviews
with 44–53; rearing practice 15–16;
testing 47–51; *see also* family; parents
Child Guidance Clinic 3, 6, 159–61
Child Psychiatric Department 3
childminding 133, 167, 169
Children and Young Persons' Acts 165,
170, 184
children's homes 167, 171
Children's Act 159
chloral 173
chlordiazepoxide 173
chlorpromazine 173
clarification in casework 123
class, social 65
classification of disorders 54–5; *see also*
causation
cohesiveness 97
colitis 82
comforters 42
communication: between agencies 4,
156–61; with child 125–6; with
colleagues 35, 153–61; with family 33;
in group play 133; patterns 16
communications theory 96–7, 118
compulsive behaviour 63
conditioning, classical 140–1, 143, 148
conduct disorders 63; *see also* anti-social
behaviour; delinquency
confidence, lack of 123
constipation 76–7
consultancy role of Child Guidance
Clinic 159–61
consultation and liaison 154–61

contra-indications in family therapy
109–10
contracts 151
co-ordination problems 78
cost-effectiveness of family approach 37
co-therapy 111–12, 137, 161
counselling: and casework 117–30; in
schools 119, 125; *see also* casework
Cruse 165
cycle of deprivation 19

day centres 5, 72, 168–9
day hospitals 168–9
day nurseries 5, 169
deafness *see* hearing problems
death of parent 15, 18, 86, 121; *see also*
separation
definition: of casework 117–18, 124; of
psychotherapy 124, 127
delinquency 56, 63–5; and counselling
119, 125; *see also* anti-social behaviour
Department of Health and Social
Security 40, 167
depression: of child 59, 174; of parents
16–17, 166
deprivation 13–19, 66
desensitization 77, 145–7
development of child 42–50; problems of
90–3; tests 47–50
diagnostic categories *see* anti-social
behaviour; emotional disorders
diazepam 70, 173
difficulties in child casework 126
discipline, poor 15, 148–9
discrimination 21, 39–40
Down's Children's Association 165
Down's Syndrome 23
Draw-a-Person test 50
drawing 31–2, 45, 50, 127
dreams 70
drinking 22, 85–6; excessive, of water 74
drugs: as medication 66, 70, 78, 172–80;
misuse 85–6; and pregnancy 23
dyphasia 92

eating *see* feeding
eczema 82
education *see* schools.
Education Act 3
electro-encephalogram 51, 78
emotional abuse 88
emotional bonds 12–19

emotional disorders 55–63; *see also*
    presenting problems
emotional state and recent health 42–4
employment, maternal 17
encopresis 75–6, 144, 146, 151
encouragement in casework 123
engaging client in casework 122–3
enuresis, nocturnal 74–5; treatment of
    143–5, 151, 174
environmental change 162–7, 180
environmental factors 3–4, 19–22, 29,
    38–40, 82, 88
Epanutin 174
Epidemiological Study 77
epilepsy 66, 174
Epilim 174
ethological theory 11
evaluation of casework 118–19, 125
example cases 176–8; of anti-social
    behaviour 148–50; of behaviour
    modification 144–8; of casework
    121–2, 125–6; of encopresis 146; of
    enuresis 144–5; of family formulation
    34–5; of family therapy 105–7, 112–15;
    of individual formulation 52–3; of
    intervention 166–7; of obsession 60–1;
    of phobia 146–8; of play therapy
    128–9; of psychotherapy 128–9

family: and adolescent 97–8, 107; and
    anti-social behaviour 64–5; assessment
    27–53, 109, 120, 177; casework 94;
    characteristics 12–19; distortion 20,
    168; large 16–17, 25, 65–6; one-parent
    18, 25; and outside world 38–40; and
    psychosomatic illness 82; relationships
    12–15, 42–50; structure 43–4; tasks 12,
    32–3; therapy 3–6, 11, 37, 62, 72, 84,
    89, 94–116; *see also* child; marital
    relationships; parents
Family Institute 116
Family Welfare Association 166, 185
*Families – application of social learning to
    family life* 149
fantasies 47
fears 55–8, 77, 141, 145–8, 173
feeding problems 71–4, 83–5, 107
financial help 165
flexibility of therapists 99
flooding 146–7
focus, limiting 123
formulation: in family assessment 34–5;

in family therapy 100, 177
fostering 90, 167, 170
frame of reference 99–112
future planning 35–6

gadget effect 143
games 135
general practitioners 157–8
general systems theory 30
generic training 4
genetic factors 22–3
gifted children 93
Gilles de la Tourette's Syndrome 80, 173
Gingerbread 165–6
Girl Guides 166
glue-sniffing 86
goals of therapy 99, 102–3
Griffiths scale 50
group tasks 134–5
group therapy 131–7
groupwork 131–2
guilt feelings 25, 122, 149

habit disorders 42, 81
haloperidol 78, 173
hallucinogens 85
handicap 9, 24, 26, 120, 166
health and emotional state 42–4
hearing problems 78, 92
history taking 28, 41–4
home: based behaviour modification
    150; family assessment at 36; removal
    from 170–1; tutors 132
homes, children's 167, 171
homosexuality 87
hospital care 3, 62, 85, 119, 158, 167–9
Housewives Register 166
housing 9, 20, 25, 66, 164
hyperkinesis 77–8, 174
hypnotics 70, 173
hysteria 61–2

illness 9, 24, 52, 62, 81–5, 158; *see also*
    handicap
imipramine 174
imitative behaviour 142–3
immature parents 15–16
immigrant status 21
inconsistency 66
incontinence *see* encopresis; enuresis
independence, need for 15
indications 109–10, 125

individual factors in anti-social
  behaviour 65–6
individual formulation 52–3
information gathering 152
insight in casework 124
Institute of Family Therapy 116
instrumental learning 141–2
intake and group work 131
intelligence 46–7, 93; quotient 48, 65,
  77–8, 86, 93, 163; tests 47–8
interval between sessions 100–1
intervention: evaluation of 8; in family
  therapy 100, 103–5, 166–7, 178–9;
  styles of 35, 51–2
interviews: with children 44–53;
  techniques 28–9, 138
IQ see intelligence
isolation of clinics 3

Kanner's Syndrome see autism
Kent Family Placement Project 170

labelling 4, 22, 54–5, 79
Largactil 78, 173
lawyers 158–9
lead poisoning 73
learning difficulties 65–6, 92–3, 156; see
  also school
learning theory 11, 60, 98, 118, 139–43
legal: obligations 108, 161; sanctions 89;
  support 158–9
length of sessions 100–2
liaison 178–80; and consultation 154–61;
  in group therapy 136–7; see also
  communication
Librium 173
life-experiences 16
lithium 174
local groups 166–7
long-term work 166–7
loss 64; see also death; separation

management of disorders: abused child
  89–90; anorexia 84–5; anti-social
  behaviour 66–7; autism 68; case
  illustration 178; depression 59; eating
  problems 71–2, 84–5; encopresis 76–7;
  enuresis 75; fears and phobias 56–8;
  hyperkinesis 78; hysteria 62;
  obsessions 61; plan and choice of
  intervention 51–3; sexual disorders 87;
  shyness 63; sleep problems 70–1

manic depression 174
mannerisms see habits; tics
MAOI see mono-amine etc.
marital: relationships 34–5, 41–4, 52–3,
  83, 88, 107, 121–2; therapy 94–116; see
  also family; parents
maternal deprivation 13–19; see also
  parents
maternal employment 17
maternity care see pregnancy
maturational theory 11
MBD see minimal brain dysfunction
medical model 28
medication see drugs
members of family in therapy 100–1, 109
mental handicap 120, 166
Merrill–Palmer scale 48
methylphenidate 174
migraine 83
minimal brain dysfunction 23–4, 78–9,
  92; see also brain
misery see depression
modelling 142
Mogadon 173
Mongolism 23, 165
mono-amine-oxidase-inhibitors 173–4
mood of child 46–7
movement problems 78
multi-axial scheme for classification 55
multi-problem families 110, 176–8
mutism, elective 62–3; see also speech
  problems
Mysoline 174

National Association for Autistic
  Children 165
National Association for Gifted Children
  93
National Association for Mentally
  Handicapped 166
National Childbirth Trust 166
National Health Service 3
national organizations 165–6
Neale Reading Test 50
neglect 88
nightmares and night terrors 70, 173
nitrazepam 173
non-accidental injury 87–9, 151; see also
  child abuse
nurseries 5, 169

obesity 72–3, 82

obsessions 60–1, 173
one-parent families 18, 25
one-way screens 110–11, 115
operant learning 141–2
opiates 88
origins of disorders *see* causation
Ospolot 174
overeating *see* obesity

paediatricians 9, 158
paradoxical techniques 109
parents: casework with 119–20; disturbed
    16–18, 26, 64, 80–1, 88–90, 166; group
    therapy with 136; use of, in behaviour
    modification 148–50; *see also* child;
    family; marital relationships
Parents Anonymous 90, 165
past, emphasis on 99
peer groups 21–2, 63
peptic ulcer 82
perception problems 78
perinatal factors *see* pregnancy
periodic syndrome 82
persistence in family therapy 108–9
phenobarbitone 174
phenytoin 174
Phergan 173
phobias 55–8, 77, 141, 145–8, 173
physical examination 51
physical factors 23–4
Piagetian theory 1, 11
pica 73
planning of casework 120–1
play 31–2, 45, 47; in groups 133–4;
    symbolic 50, 133; tests 50; as therapy
    127–9, 132–4
playgroups 132, 167
poisoning 73, 88
political theory 118
polydypsia 74
post-natal period 23; *see also* pregnancy
poverty 19–20, 52–3, 65, 164–5
practical considerations of family therapy
    98–9
pregnancy 9, 23, 42, 88, 166
prejudice 21
prenatal factors *see* pregnancy
present, emphasis on 99
presenting problems 41–2, 44, 54–93
prevention 8–9
primidone 174
Prisoners' Wives and Families'

Association 165–6
privation 14; *see also* deprivation
progress evaluation 100, 105–6
'projective' tests 50–1
psychoanalysis 84; defined 127; and
    family therapy 3, 11, 95–6
psychoses 67–9
psychosomatic problems 81–3
psychotherapy 62, 66, 84; defined 124,
    127; individual 126–30; *see also* family
    therapy

Raven's Matrices 48
reading: problems 91, 156; tests 50
recording problems 152
referrals 4, 136, 160
regression 84
reinforcements 134, 142
relationships *see* communication; family;
    marital relationships
remarriage 121–2
removal from home 170–1
Repertory Grids 51
research 7–8
resistance to therapy 108–10, 122
resource systems 39–40
respondent learning 140–1
responsibility of family 106–7
Reynell Developmental Language Scale
    50
rewards 141–5, 148
Ritalin 78, 174
rituals, bedtime 69
role-playing 110–11, 135
role reversal 88
rural life 20

sample cases *see* examples
scapegoating 88, 122
schizophrenia 96–7
school: adjustment 43–4; changes in
    162–4; consultancy in 156–7;
    counselling in 119, 125; effect of 9, 21,
    38–9, 65–6; group therapy in 134;
    phobia 56–8, 147–8; and
    psychosomatic illness 82; special 163;
    teachers 150, 156–7; *see also* learning
    difficulties
secure base 14–15
sedatives 173
separation 12–14, 25, 147; *see also* death
Serenace 173

session frequency and duration 101–2
sexual abuse 88
sexual development 43–4
sexual differences in disorders 24, 65–6, 80, 83, 91
sexual disorders 86–7
sexual identity 110
short-term work 4, 119
shyness 62–3
siblings 44, 46, 149–50; *see also* family
sleep problems 69–71
sleeping drugs 70, 173
slimming *see* anorexia; obesity
smoking 85
social factors 65
social service departments 4, 37
social work contribution 6–7
social worker's role 143–4
socio-cultural factors 19–22; *see also* environmental factors
sodium valproate 174
solvent abuse 86
specialization 6–7
speech 46–7; problems 42, 48, 62, 78, 92; tests 50; in therapy 135–6
stages of casework 120–3
stammering 80–1
Stanford-Binet test 48
statutory obligations 108, 161; *see also* legal
stealing 63
Stelazine 173
stimulus response 140–3; *see also* conditioning
strategies of casework 123–4
stress 55
structural relationships 32
structural theory 32, 97–8
stuttering 80–1
sub-systems 32, 97, 105, 110
suicide 59
sulthiame 174
supervision 110–12
support groups 165–7
symbolic play 50, 133

talk *see* speech
talking therapy groups 135–6

tasks 123; family 12, 32–3; group 134–5
teachers 150, 156–7; *see also* schools
Tegretol 174
temperamental characteristics 24–5
termination: of casework 124; of family therapy 112
testing 47–51
theoretical considerations of family therapy 95–8
theoretical orientation of therapists 98
therapeutic goals 100, 102–3
therapists: characteristics 98–100; involvement 33
thought processes of child 46–7
tics 42, 79–80, 173
time, length of, in therapy 100, 102, 124, 128
'time-out' 150
Tofranil 75, 174
toilet phobia 144, 146; *see also* encopresis; enuresis
training 4, 135
tranquillizers 78, 85, 173
transactional patterns 97
transference 134
tricyclics 173–4
trifluoperazine 173
Tryptizol 75, 174
truancy 56; *see also* school
Turner's Syndrome 23

underachievement 92–3
unhappiness *see* depression
United States 3, 48, 79, 150, 170
urban life 20, 64

Valium 70, 173
Vallergan 173
ventilation 123
videotape 110–11

waiting lists 3
'walk-in' clinics 4
Wechsler scales 48
WISC-R *see* Wechsler
withdrawal 62–3
working mother 17
WPPSI *see* Wechsler